Alan Crook was born in 1942 into a family of Methodists of several generations.

He has been a Local Preacher of the Methodist Church since 1964. After working for some years as a Teacher and Linguist, and voluntarily as a trained Counsellor, he trained in Homœopathy at the College of Homœopathy, London, receiving his Licentiate in 1984. Since 1987 he has been a member of the Register of the Society of Homœopaths, of which he was later a Director until joining the staff of the College of Homœopathy. He is now Director of Studies at that College, while continuing to practise part-time, and also translates books on Homœopathy from German into English. Alan is married with three sons and lives in Sussex.

A
CHRISTIAN'S
GUIDE TO
HOMŒOPATHY

by
Alan Crook. MA, MCH, RSHom.

Winter Press
29 Horniman Drive
London SE23 3BJ

First published by Winter Press in 1996

Copyright Alan Crook 1996

ISBN 1 874581 03 7

Cover design by Colin Winter

Printed by Biddles of Guildford, Surrey

CONTENTS

ACKNOWLEDGEMENTS

I should like to thank Louise Deacon for unwittingly being the catalyst of this whole project, and Mike Taylor for the detailed correspondence which was instrumental in shaping my initial thoughts.

Thanks are also due to a number of people who kindly read through the manuscript and made suggestions for improvements: my wife Pam, Roger Dyson, Ray Edwards, Christine and John Huggett of P.A.C.T., Roy Lenton, John Morgan and Mike Strange. I have been encouraged by my family and a number of homoeopathic colleagues while working on this book, and in particular by Susan Curtis and Colin Winter of Winter Press, whose benign guidance has been valuable and greatly appreciated.

I must also acknowledge the debt that I owe those writers, researchers and lecturers who guided my homoeopathic studies and were influential in shaping my thinking, not only those mentioned in the references and footnotes, but the staff of the College of Homoeopathy 1981-85 and those whose lectures and seminars I have attended since.

Finally my undying thanks must go to my parents, grandparents and all those fellow-Christians who have done so much to lay the foundations of my own Christian faith and to strengthen it and give it direction over the years.

FOREWORD

I first became aware of Homœopathy — and Natural Therapies generally — in the late 1970's, and was guided by a series of apparent coincidences to study it, and then to leave my work as a teacher and linguist in order to practise it. I also came to homœopathic practice from a Christian background, having been brought up in a Methodist family, and having been accredited as a Local Preacher in 1964. In study groups at my home church, then as a student at university (where "demythologisation" was the theological buzz-word), and later when teaching R.E. to sceptical young people, I was forced to think about and re-examine my beliefs, so that they became a living part of myself rather than merely something which had been drummed into me from an early age and accepted unquestioningly. Both at university and when I later spent some time living abroad, worshipping and preaching within different Christian denominations, I learned that there are different ways of incorporating a framework of beliefs into one's way of life, different ways of worshipping one's God, and different ways of interpreting eternal truths so that they remain relevant to contemporary life.

A few years after I had trained and gone into practice, my mother showed me a booklet entitled "Homœopathy" which she had purchased in a Christian bookshop, and whose contents she had found somewhat disturbing. It turned out to be a translation into English of a booklet by a Dr. H.J. Bopp of Neuchâtel, Switzerland, which attacked Homœopathy as "dangerous" and "occult". At the time I wrote a rather dismissive critique of it for a small, privately circulated periodical called "Lesser Writings", which was read by homœopaths and students of Homœopathy, and then put it out of my mind.

Some years later I joined the staff of the College of Homœopathy in London, where I was approached by a student who had encountered Christian objections to Homœopathy. I gave her a copy of my article from "Lesser Writings", which she showed to a colleague at the hospital where she worked. He was very much involved in the critique of therapies and practices perceived to be "occult", and I was soon drawn into a correspondence which revealed to me the measure of the misapprehension shared by some Christians regarding the nature of Homœopathy and other "alternative" medical modalities.

This dialogue with Mike Taylor helped to give shape to the thoughts and arguments which were the foundation of this book. Other members of the Society of Homœopaths have increasingly expressed concern to me regarding Christian misrepresentation of a therapy which I have found to be supremely compatible with my Christian beliefs. Most of the Christian criticism of Homœopathy seems to have originated within the establishment of Western "orthodox" medicine (known to homœopaths as "Allopathy"), and has a strong allopathic flavour. The information supplied about Homœopathy is not always accurate, especially with regard to practice in the UK. I therefore considered that the time had come to write, with the support and encouragement of some of my colleagues, a book which examines the relationship of Christianity and Homœopathy from the point of view of someone who practises and understands both, and which looks critically at some of the objections which have been raised.

These objections frequently suggest that there is something supernatural about Homœopathy, and that this is why it should be approached with caution by Christians. I hope to show in this book that this is far from being the case. It was St. Augustine who is reported to have said: "Miracles do not happen in contradiction of nature, but in contradiction of what we know about nature." Exciting new discoveries are still being made about the natural world and its energies and, indeed, about human beings and how they function. There is much for which science still has no explanation: just one example is the ability of pigeons to home, and the ability of some pets to home in on their owners even when separated from them by a distance of hundreds of miles. So long as mysteries such as these remain unsolved by science, I do not believe that it is justifiable for the scientific establishment to dismiss any phenomenon as "unscientific". Thus it is my hope that this book will liberate many who have been made suspicious of Homœopathy to accept it as yet one more positive aspect of God's creation and one of His generous gifts for the benefit of human kind. Indeed, plausible scientific explanations already exist for the effectiveness of Homœopathy, and I have also tried to describe these in the following pages. Please read with an open mind.

INTRODUCTION

Someone once said that there can be no greater chasm between two people than the chasm of belief. Certainly much blood has been shed in the course of human history because individuals or nations perceived a threat to their belief-system, religious, political or whatever. In writing this book I am aware that there will be some people who will refuse even to consider my argument because, regarding Homœopathy, their minds are closed to any interpretation of the truth other than their own. They occupy an entrenched position, and to shift from it would require courage: courage to risk the disapproval of their fellow-believers, courage to feel adventurous, exposed and insecure for a while as they sought to re-define their beliefs. My prayer for them is that they will at least have the courage to give this book a reading and to try to set down in writing what it is about it that they disagree with, and why. These are issues which cry out for serious consideration.

This book has been written primarily with those Christians in mind who think seriously about issues of the Christian life and the Christian faith. Alternative and Complementary Medicine is an area about which conflicting views are frequently expressed in the media and elsewhere, outside the religious arena and, as is also the case with political issues, these views may often become polarised with a strength and degree of conviction which is akin to religious belief.

Within the Church it is also not uncommon for individuals who have made choices in their lives to try to justify these choices by projecting them on to the Church at large. Thus, for example,

1

someone who has become a Socialist or a teetotaller may propagate the view that Socialism or total abstinence is the only acceptable choice for any true Christian, and that someone who holds a divergent view cannot be a "proper" Christian, or even a Christian at all. The same may apply in the case of a particular type of religious experience or encounter with God.

A small number of Christians have chosen to project their own medical or scientific prejudice on to the Christian faith in a similar way, rationalising or justifying their position by suggesting that Homœopathy in particular, or Alternative and Complementary Medicine in general, are a part of the occult or satanic scene, against which there is something of a crusade among Christian evangelicals. Such a suggestion is guaranteed to push alarm buttons for many Christian believers.

Whilst the originators of this line of thought were no doubt sincere in their beliefs, sadly their objectivity has been clouded by their medical or scientific prejudice, and their argument was based on a fundamental misunderstanding of certain natural phenomena and an ignorance of recent scientific studies. This has resulted in serious misrepresentation of the nature of homœopathic medicine and the creation in many Christians of a mental association which, tragically, has deprived them of its benefits.

The aim of this book is to provide accurate information regarding Homœopathy, and an analysis of the main Christian objections to it, so that thinking and enquiring Christians may reach a balanced and informed decision as to whether homœopathic treatment is compatible with their Christian faith. If it also helps some of the objectors towards an informed reconsideration of their position, that will be an added bonus. It is written by someone who is both a Christian and a fully qualified Registered Homœopath, in the hope that it will prove helpful to Christians who are seeking a gentle but effective way of improving their level of health. It will also examine some misconceptions regarding Homœopathy which are currently held and propagated by some members of the Church, and which might unnecessarily deter Christians from finding healing through this branch of medicine.

WHY SHOULD CHRISTIANS BE CONCERNED ABOUT HEALTHCARE?

For the duration of this life we are given only one body. Whilst most Christians consider the spirit more important than the body, at the same time we believe that the body is the temple of the Holy Spirit, who dwells within us, (I Cor.6:19) and that it should therefore be treated with the greatest possible reverence and respect. Some would also argue that we should exercise good stewardship of this body which God has entrusted to us, by protecting it whenever possible from abuse or damage.

In the past devout Christians believed that they could improve the spiritual quality of their lives by disciplining their bodies. Maybe they had in mind St. Paul's words (I Cor. 9:27): "I harden my body with blows and bring it under complete control, to keep myself from being disqualified after having called others to the contest." Thus practices such as flagellation became fashionable among the devout and in monastic orders, and the flesh was subdued by harsh treatment. Puritanism forbade many activities which had generally been considered pleasurable.

In more modern times we have seen a burgeoning of concern among many people regarding the fitness of their bodies. Dieting and fasting, keep-fit, aerobics and jogging, or sports have all become popular, not so much as a spiritual discipline, but more as a means of maintaining physical health, and with it mental health as well. The mental and emotional stresses to which many are exposed in the course of their work, or in difficult relationships, take their toll in terms of the adrenalin which cannot be worked off by "fight or flight", as it was in our ancient ancestors when they met a mammoth or a sabre-toothed tiger in the course of a day's hunting. If it is not worked off in some aerobic activity, this extra energy is stored and in the long term can damage the health, with repercussions on the tissues or the immune system. (There is evidence that, in the long term, unused adrenalin in the system interferes with the production of T-lymphocytes, which play an important role in the function of the immune system.)

As well as the active methods just described, there are other less energetic ways of counteracting a stressful life. Those who

3

are stressed and tense can benefit tremendously from intensive relaxation, either with the aid of specially prepared tapes, or through such therapies as massage or aromatherapy. These may be perceived as too expensive, but basic massage techniques are easily learnt and this is something which couples or friends can do for each other, and which may also enrich a relationship.

Thus there are many ways in which Christians can consciously take care of their bodies. Clearly we can also avoid obvious abuses of the body such as smoking, social drug abuse, casual sexual intimacy or immoderate eating and alcohol consumption. And yet so often we appear to have a blind spot in one particular respect. This occurs when it comes to medical treatment.

For centuries, traditional medical treatment in the West consisted mainly of herbal remedies. Gradually, however, allopathic or "orthodox" medicine began to prevail. For a time, chemical treatments became fashionable, involving the use of grossly toxic substances such as mercury, and also violent methods such as purging and blood-letting. Then, as the modern chemical and pharmaceutical industries developed, it became possible to synthesise the chemicals which occur in herbs and which are perceived to be their active constituents. Deprived of the other constituents found in the whole herb which act as buffers and catalysts, these synthesised drugs frequently have severe side-effects, so that the correct dosage becomes critical. Rigorous tests and trials are carried out before any new drug is permitted on the market. Sadly, in spite of these precautions, something like 15,000 people die each year in the UK. as a result of therapeutic drug complications (3 times more than die on the roads), whilst in the USA 60,000 deaths occur annually from the administration of clinical drugs in hospitals.

Doctors who prescribe these drugs have to take account of a "risk-benefit ratio". They have to ask themselves whether the benefit to the patient outweighs the risk of administering the substance. Taking most drugs involves an element of risk: risk of unpleasant side-effects at least, if not complications. And this is a risk which most people appear willing to take.

And yet effective alternatives exist which do not carry this risk. There can be few people who have not heard of

"Alternative and Complementary Medicine", though maybe they do not know exactly what it means†. This book is about one of these alternative therapies: Homœopathy. There are many introductory books which have been written on this subject in recent years and are available in bookshops. Some give detailed guidance on how to select remedies in order to treat yourself. This book does not set out to cover that ground again. It looks at Homœopathy particularly from the Christian point of view and aims to answer questions which Christians might ask regarding the suitability of Homœopathy for keeping them in good health.

---

† Although these terms are often used interchangeably, there is a difference. Complementary therapies are those which complement orthodox medicine and can be used alongside it: most of the physical therapies such as Osteopathy, Chiropractic, Physiotherapy, Aromatherapy, etc. would come under this heading. Alternative therapies are those whose philosophies have a radically different understanding of the nature of health and disease, or a different basis from that of orthodox medicine, and cannot normally be successfully used alongside it. These would include Homœopathy, Chinese Medicine and possibly Herbal Medicine, although there are some exceptions, e.g. the use of Acupuncture as an alternative anæsthetic during surgery; the use of homœopathic Symphytum to accelerate the union of fractures once these have been set in the orthodox way.

CHAPTER 1

WHAT IS HOMŒOPATHY?

Homœopathy is a system of medicine which gently assists the body in its task of self-healing. It regards the production of symptoms as part of this effort by the body to heal itself. It works by giving tiny doses of a substance which, when taken by someone in full health, would produce these same symptoms.

Science has shown that all the functions of the body on its different levels (physical, emotional and mental) are governed by electromagnetic energy-fields(1). When the body's immune response is weakened by some change to which it is unable to adapt, and disease gains the upper hand, the resonance of these energy-fields is disturbed, and symptoms result from this disturbance. A homœopath notes all these symptoms carefully and matches them as closely as possible with the combination of symptoms produced by one of the remedies when they are "proved" or tried out by healthy human volunteers. (Trials on animals are neither necessary nor useful, as animals do not necessarily react in the same way as humans.) The energy pattern of the substance indicated by the patient's symptoms is able gently to re-establish the correct resonance of the energy-fields and thus to restore health. Once health is restored, the symptoms become redundant and go away.

So you see that Homœopathy is not about killing germs or

treating symptoms; it is about restoring health. It aims to heal the whole person and therefore, in the case-taking, all aspects of the patient are addressed. It is important to know how the patient interacts with his or her environment and with other people, because health is not just the absence of illness. It is a state of positive well-being and vitality, in which our interface with the world outside us is just as important as what goes on inside.

Above all, homœopathic remedies treat the patient gently and with reverence. It is impossible to become addicted to them, nor do they produce side-effects which might leave patients sicker than they were before. Frequently a homœopathic treatment may result in a detoxification by the body. Conditions which had previously been driven inwards ("suppressed") by medication may work their way outwards again, cleansing the body of toxic material which is better out than in. This may be temporarily unpleasant, but is in no way harmful. On the contrary, it leaves the body healthier and stronger.

An example of this might be asthma, following the suppression of eczema by skin creams. When the correct homœopathic remedy is taken, the asthma should recover first, and it is highly likely that the earlier eczema will reappear for a while, eventually disappearing altogether. Healing has taken place. The disease has been "cast out" of the body, which of course has a biblical precedent. Thus you see that homœopaths have a standard by which to judge and assess their treatments. Having given the remedy, they take careful note of what happens, and hope to see the focus of the disease moving from within outwards, and from more important organs or systems of the body to less important ones. Often old symptoms will reappear briefly, as if to wave goodbye, in the reverse order of their original occurrence. Sometimes symptoms are also observed to move from above downwards on their way out. Should a treatment result in a movement which contradicts these directions (e.g. a skin eruption clears up but the patient becomes mentally irritable), then a trained homœopath will know that suppression is occurring, which will lead to an unhealthier state; and so the treatment must be antidoted and a new approach to the case must be adopted.

The way in which the remedies are prepared (see Appendix I)

is very cost-effective compared with that of pharmaceutical drugs, although the initial consultation will normally take considerably longer than in orthodox medicine ("Allopathy"), thus offsetting the lower cost of the medication. However, the greater difference lies in the fact that under homœopathic treatment the patient's health improves, making ongoing treatment decreasingly necessary. With allopathic treatment, on the contrary, the effect of drugs is to weaken the body or, by suppressing acute conditions, to lead to more chronic ones, as the focus of the disease is driven inwards. The cost-effectiveness of Homœopathy was well illustrated in 1972, when the government of West Bengal asked homœopaths to share in the treatment of refugees from the war in Bangladesh, many of whom were suffering from cholera. Under allopathic treatment, 34% of the cholera patients recovered at a cost of £1.50 per patient. In contrast to this, 92% of those treated homœopathically were cured, at a cost of 0.5p per patient!

However, Homœopathy does not require a disease to be diagnosed. For a homœopath, the only diagnosis necessary is that of the remedy indicated by the symptoms. Disease labels are not helpful to the homœopath, so long as he or she understands the disease process which is going on within the patient. Several patients suffering from the same illness might receive totally different remedies, because they were totally different types of people. Thus people can be helped with Homœopathy who are not suffering from any recognised illness. They may have been told that there is nothing wrong with them, the test results may all have been negative, they may have been told that "it is all in the mind", or that they "must learn to live with it". Because Homœopathy treats each patient as an individual, looks for what is unique, different or unusual, and tailors the prescription to the perceived symptoms, and does not seek to place people in pigeonholes, it is very often able to help people who have found no hope elsewhere. (It is also true to say that it would usually be much easier to treat such people if they came for Homœopathy in the first place! A regime of drugs in the recent past can make homœopathic prescribing less straightforward, whilst drugs which cannot be discontinued make it downright complicated!)

Homœopathic treatment is available in many countries. In

some, it is only available from allopathically trained doctors who have re-trained in Homœopathy. Because the philosophies of these two schools of medicine are so opposed to each other, this does present problems of re-orientation and it is not uncommon for doctors to show a tendency to prescribe remedies for illnesses rather than holistically, although some have embraced the homœopathic philosophy wholeheartedly. As explained in the next chapter, the UK. is fortunate in also having a tradition of non-allopathically trained homœopaths, who have attended colleges specifically established to teach Homœopathy with the necessary knowledge of human sciences but without the encumbrance of allopathic philosophy and its insistence on diagnosis of illness and the use of drugs. With very few exceptions, treatment from professional homœopaths is not yet available within the National Health Service, but some more progressive private Health Insurance companies are now offering reimbursement for professional homœopathic treatment.

A number of books are available which offer help with self-selection of remedies, and low-potency remedies are increasingly available from pharmacies and healthfood stores. Many families and individuals have become quite adept at using these books and remedies in straightforward illnesses. However, it is important to bear in mind the rules of cure mentioned above and to seek professional help if the focus of a problem appears to be shifting to a more vital organ or symptom. Another important feature of homœopathic medication is that it should be discontinued as soon as cure appears to be underway. There is no question of "finishing the course". And if a remedy is having no effect at all it should also be discontinued and a different one selected. To persist in taking the wrong remedy over a long period of time could possibly result in producing some unwanted symptoms. It must also be borne in mind that there is a wide range of potencies available to professionals, which is not stocked by ordinary pharmacies or healthfood shops. Deep-rooted conditions, especially those affecting the mind and emotions, are best treated professionally with the higher potencies.

Thus it should be clear that there are many levels of homœopathic treatment, from simple first-aid via straightforward acute illness to the very deepest levels of disease where even the patient's will to live is compromised. Whilst it is possible to achieve proficiency up to a certain level with the aid of self-help books and a home remedy-kit, there are also practitioners who spend a lifetime perfecting the art and science of healing at the deepest levels. Whilst there are strictly speaking no "specialists" within Homœopathy, some may acquire a reputation for helping effectively in particular types of case. In the UK. there is a professional association for qualified homœopaths: The Society of Homœopaths. The Society publishes a register of homœopaths who have satisfied its registration standards and agreed to abide by its codes of ethics and practice. Most of these will have been trained at one of the Colleges of Homœopathy, the first of which was founded in 1978. In Chapter 2 we see how Homœopathy progressed to that point.

REFERENCES:

1. See, for example, Burr, H. S., "The Fields of Life", (New York: Ballantine, 1972).

HOW HOMŒOPATHY DEVELOPED

The Greek physician and teacher Hippocrates (4th century B.C.) is generally regarded as the Father of Modern Medicine, and doctors still swear the oath which bears his name. In fact he was aware of two ways of healing: the way of Similars and the way of Opposites. He emphasised the importance of accurate observation of the patient, saying: "I would rather know what kind of person has a disease than what kind of disease a person has."

The way of Opposites is well-known to those who are treated by Allopathy: If you have a pain you are given a painkiller; if you cannot sleep, you are given something to induce sleep; if you have a fever, you are given something to lower your temperature, and so on.

The way of Similars is rather different: something is given which, in a healthy person, would produce the same set of symptoms as those of which the patient complains. Because symptoms are the body's way of trying to heal the disturbance to its health, giving a small dose of something which causes those symptoms and reinforces them will assist the body in its attempt to heal itself, and bring about healing in a natural, non-violent way.

After the death of Hippocrates it was the way of Opposites which achieved greater popularity in Europe, and the way of Similars went underground as "folk-medicine", only coming up briefly for an airing at the time of Paracelsus (1493-1541). Two centuries later, in the German town of Meissen, Samuel Hahnemann was born. His father was a painter of Dresden porcelain. Shortly after Samuel's birth, the porcelain industry collapsed as a result of military action and much of Samuel's education took place at home. His father's methods included setting him a problem in the morning, then locking him in his room until he had solved it!

Thus early in his life he learned to think creatively and independently. When he did receive formal education, those who taught him recognised his ability, and he was able to obtain sponsorship for his university medical studies. Having received his Doctorate of Medicine, however, he was soon to give up his chosen career on grounds of conscience. He felt increasingly unable to apply the methods and toxic medicines which were employed by Allopathy at that time, and he observed that patients stood a better chance of recovery without treatment than with it. As he was also a brilliant chemist and linguist, he turned increasingly to these fields to support himself and his family. It was while he was translating an article on quinine by the Scottish professor Cullen that his turning point came.

Dissatisfied by Cullen's explanation of the action of quinine in the treatment of malaria, Hahnemann decided to carry out a little self-experimentation. He soon found that, by taking regular doses of Peruvian bark ("China"), the source of quinine, he developed symptoms of malaria. That this was not genuine malaria was clear from the fact that when he stopped taking the substance, the symptoms departed. Thus he deduced that the reason why this substance was successful in curing malaria was that, in a healthy person, it produced the symptoms of that disease.

We have seen that the Principle of Similars had already been known and used for centuries. Hahnemann's contribution was to take this principle and organise it into a workable, methodical system of medicine. As he experimented with more and more substances, some of them highly toxic, he sought a way of sparing the patients the inevitable side-effects and suffering and, like Paracelsus, he came upon the idea of reducing the size of the doses. Unknown to himself, since there were no instruments to measure such things, in diluting his medicines he went beyond the point at which any molecules of the original substance remain. And yet the medicines were still active.

One day a vial of medicine fell unnoticed to the floor of his carriage and remained there for some time, receiving a good shaking-up from the combination of poor suspension and unmade German roads. When Hahnemann eventually retrieved it and started using it again, he noticed that it was now even more effective in treatment. In this way he intuitively hit upon the idea of "dynamizing" his medicines as he diluted them, by hitting the vial repeatedly against the back of a leather-bound book. Thus, the weaker they became in physical terms, the more energy was transferred to them. Somehow the diluted preparation retained a memory of the energy-pattern of the original substance †.

Cautiously Hahnemann started applying in medical practice the principles which he was formulating, and found that they worked. In 1796 he published an essay in which the word "Homœopathy" was first used and, in 1810, he published the first edition of his "Organon of the Rational Art of Healing". Because of his insistence that only one medicine at a time should be prescribed, and only in tiny quantities at that, he soon fell foul of the apothecaries as well as the allopathic doctors, and their opposition resulted in several enforced moves from places where he was no longer permitted to practice.

Gradually he built up a following of friends and pupils, who tried out or "proved" a growing number of new remedies and prescribed them according to homœopathic principles. Visitors came from overseas, among them a Dr. Quin of London, who set up an influential practice and also founded the London Homœopathic Hospital and what was later to become the

† This phenomenon, which is probably the main stumbling-block for the majority of orthodox scientists who might otherwise accept Homœopathy, has more recently been demonstrated under laboratory conditions by the French scientist, Jacques Benveniste, and replicated in other laboratories in several countries. (See Appendix I)

Faculty of Homœopathy. Homœopaths such as Constantine Hering travelled to America, and for many years there was a thriving homœopathic profession there with numerous hospitals, and colleges which also — unusually at that time — admitted women and black students.

Many of the herbal remedies of the native American tribes were proved and added to the homœopathic materia medica. Then the American Medical Association was formed by allopathic doctors, and mounted a sustained campaign that resulted in legislative discrimination against the colleges and their graduates, and Homœopathy gradually declined until quite recently, when there has been a revival. French settlers took Homœopathy to India, where it became very popular and is now one of the three officially recognised medical modalities, along with Allopathy and Ayurvedic Medicine.

In Britain, Homœopathy has survived various attempts to outlaw it, and the strong disapproval of the allopathic establishment, and is now actually accessible in some areas on the National Health Service. Tragically, many eminent homœopathic doctors died in the 1972 Staines air crash. However, a feature of homœopathy in Britain has been the development since the 1970's of a Homœopathic profession whose members are not allopathically qualified doctors. Their professional association, the Society of Homœopaths, has its own Register, Codes of Ethics and Practice, and disciplinary procedures. A number of colleges have also been established, teaching "classical Homœopathy" to a very high standard with 3-year full-time or 4-year part-time courses. These include a significant element of human sciences (Anatomy, Physiology, Human Dysfunction).

A number of international teachers of high calibre have emerged, with the result that homœopathic treatment of the highest professional standard is becoming more widely available year after year, and this pattern is being repeated in many European countries. There is also an increasing trend towards domestic use of Homœopathy, using self-help books and over-the-counter remedies. Doctors too are showing increasing interest and are either attending courses themselves or buying in the services of professional homœopaths.

The B.M.A., which only a few years ago published a report in which virtually all natural therapies were dismissed as "placebo effect"(1), is now speaking of "discrete clinical disciplines" deserving of greater research funding and statutory regulation(2). By "discrete clinical disciplines" they mean therapies distinguished from other modalities by having more established foundations of training, competence and professional standards, and which have the greatest potential for use alongside orthodox medical care.

Classical Homœopathy (so called to distinguish it from Complex Homœopathy which uses several remedies combined into one dose) is essentially a holistic therapy. That is to say, it treats people rather than diagnosed diseases, and it recognises that people function on several levels: spiritual, mental, emotional and physical. The primary focus of a patient's disorder may lie on any of these levels, but all the levels are taken into account in prescribing. In other words, the whole person is treated, hence the use of the word "(w)holistic".

In common with all the major medical systems of the world with the exception of Allopathy, Homœopathy recognises the existence and importance of electromagnetic energy in human function. This phenomenon has been given various names in the different medical traditions. In the homœopathic tradition it is known as "Vital Force" or "Dynamis". Since this occupies a central place in some Christian critiques of Homœopathy it will be discussed in a chapter of its own. At this point it is sufficient to mention that the patient's level of Vital Force plays an important role in determining the dosage of the remedy, and its "potency" in particular.

The potency of a remedy is the number of stages of dilution and succussion (the process of dynamization) through which it has proceeded, as described in Appendix I. Thus a "low potency" has only been through a few dilutions (1:100 or 1:10) and may still have some molecules of the original substance in it. A "high potency" has been through many stages, and will contain only the energy-pattern of the original substance, plus the vehicle (lactose or ethanol) in which it is dispensed.

It is fair to say that dynamization or potentization has been the subject of controversy within the homœopathic profession as well as outside it. Whilst the American homœopaths were reeling under the onslaught of the A.M.A., their professional immunity was severely compromised by internal arguments over this issue, which undoubtedly hastened their demise. Such polarisation is unnecessary. Both low and high potencies have their uses depending on the needs of the patient. Neither is absolutely right or wrong, and anyone who abstains from prescribing at either end of the potency-range for doctrinaire reasons will be handicapped in their treatment of certain cases. Such doctrinaire reasons usually proceed from a lack of understanding of the nature of the potencies and of health and disease.

Because homœopathic remedies are prescribed in a holistic way — for people, not for diseases — there have been a number of problems regarding their licensing. Allopathic drugs are prescribed for diagnosed conditions, often to kill a particular germ which is held to be the cause of the disease. Because they are potentially dangerous, their dosage has to be carefully controlled, and they are prescribed on a basis of "risk-benefit ratio", as mentioned in the Introduction. All drugs undergo thorough trials.

The trial of choice is normally the "double-blind crossover placebo-controlled" trial. Here a group of patients (or laboratory animals) is given the drug, and another group is given a placebo (unmedicated pill). Neither the group members nor the person giving the drug to them knows which group is getting which. At a certain point (the "crossover"), the groups are switched. Thus it should be possible to assess whether the group receiving the drug is doing better than the control group, which receives the placebo. (This is discussed further in Chapter 4).

Those in charge of the important task of licensing new drugs, and others in the orthodox scientific establishment, have been inclined to say that natural medicines should undergo the same trials as drugs, regardless of their long tradition of safe use. This disregards the fact that homœopathic remedies are not prescribed for diseases, and that a group of patients suffering from disease X will very likely receive a variety of different remedies, according to their holistic symptom-pictures.

Most of the research studies which have been carried out so far have demonstrated that potentized remedies (e.g. potentized pollens for hay fever sufferers) are statistically more effective than placebo. This demonstrates the effectiveness of the remedies, but not the method, since a remedy is only homœopathic if it is prescribed for the individual patient.

Rather than devising realistic research protocols suited to the system under evaluation, many scientists have appeared to take a perverse delight in refusing to accept Homœopathy until it satisfies the allopathic criteria. However, recently the European Community has passed a directive which, after some effort on the part of professionals and consumers, has officially recognised that homœopathic single remedies are not prescribed for diseases. Thus, so long as they bear only their name, and no therapeutic indications, they will only have to satisfy criteria of purity of origin and not go through the procedures described above, which would have placed a crippling financial burden on the manufacturing pharmacies.

The homœopathic profession requires a full range of remedies to be available, mostly in a wide range of potencies. These cannot be patented and some of them are seldom used, and their production would never be commercially viable if subject to the full trials and licensing costs of lucrative pharmaceutical drugs. Such an imposition would also have removed one of the great advantages of homœopathic treatment for the consumer (and also for the National Health Service, if it were to adopt homœopathic treatment on a wide scale): the low cost of the remedies.

Homœopathic practice varies considerably within the countries of the European Community, so much so that up to now it has not been possible to harmonise it. At the present time there are homœopathic doctors in many countries. In some there are also professional homœopaths with expert training, and the European Council for Classical Homœopathy is proceeding with the task of standardising the professional training in such countries.

In other countries any kind of medical practice is restricted by law to those with a degree in allopathic medicine. In a number of countries, including the U.K., there are a number of lay practitioners without formal training. Some of these have considerable healing gifts. From time to time one hears of others who exploit their patients in an unethical way and whose standards of practice are questionable. Without regulation, patients have little or no redress against such practitioners unless the law has been broken. It seems likely that at some time in the future legislative regulation will exclude such people from practice.

A further problem yet to be addressed is that of allopathic doctors who receive a perfunctory familiarisation of a few weekends in some natural therapy and then regard themselves as qualified to practice it. The 1993 B.M.A. report refers to the need for high standards for all who practice "complementary" therapies, and it is to be hoped that they will address this issue among their own members. Recently, welcome and significant improvements have been implemented in the post-graduate homœopathic training structure for doctors.

REFERENCES:

1. *Alternative Medicine* — a report of the Board of Science and Education, B.M.A. 1986.
2. *Complementary Medicine: New Approaches to Good Practice* B.M.A., 1993.

ENERGY MEDICINE AND THE "VITAL FORCE"

Although electricity supply companies have traditionally tended to deny the fact, it is now acknowledged that people who live underneath overhead power cables become ill. Nine studies have shown that, where there is residential exposure to electromagnetic fields from power lines, there is an increased risk of childhood cancer. Exposed to a strong electro-magnetic energy field, the health of the human organism becomes disordered(1). There is also evidence that this happens when the source of the energy field is underground, resulting in so-called geopathic stress(2).

At Salford University, Dr. Cyril Smith has found that patients suffering from allergies can be cured if they carry around with them a vial of liquid charged with the electro-magnetic frequency of the substance to which they are allergic(3).

From the above it appears that the health of the human organism can be both adversely and beneficially affected by external electro-magnetic energy fields (EMF's). Extensive studies by two American scientists, Harold Burr(4) and Leonard

Ravitz, at Yale University some years ago showed that all living beings possess a complex electro-magnetic energy field, and that it is this EMF which actually controls the biochemical processes of our bodies and gives order and structure to them.

Left to its own devices, the tendency of biochemistry is to gradually run down and eventually decay. It requires a vector force — a continuous energy injection — to keep it moving, and this force is provided by its controlling electromagnetic energy field. If this is disordered, if something happens to change the frequency at which it resonates, then the health of the person will also be disordered. The scientific discipline which studies such phenomena is known as Biophysics.

Long before scientists were able to investigate this phenomenon objectively, those who concerned themselves with matters of health were intuitively aware of it. Semantics — the science of meaning — shows us that the vocabulary of a language reflects reality as it is experienced by those who speak it. (For example, Arabic has several words for "camel"; the Eskimos have several words for "snow"; English has several words for things used to hit a ball in a variety of sports!) Thus in the medical traditions and philosophies of different cultures, words came into use to refer to the energy which governs how we function.

In the ancient Chinese tradition it was referred to as "Qi" (Chi), in the Indian tradition as "Prana". In the homœopathic tradition Hahnemann referred to it as the "Dynamis" or Vital Force, and he described in some detail, before the discoveries of Burr and Ravitz, how it rules the functions of the human organism and how, when it is disordered, the health of the organism also becomes disordered(5). By restoring order to the Vital Force, he said, health can be restored to the patient. Health is a dynamic state, and requires dynamic remedies to restore its functions. Hence the importance which he attached to "dynamizing" or potentizing the remedies when serially diluting them.

The French philosopher René Descartes was responsible for re-shaping medical thinking in the Western tradition along strictly materialistic lines. He compared a sick person with an ill-made clock, and a healthy person with a well-made clock (6). Thus health was purely a matter of mechanical function. In case of malfunction, the offending part could be repaired or replaced, with no need to consider the possibility of repercussions in any of the other parts. Intangible considerations such as the emotions, the spirit, and any idea of Vital Force, no longer had a place in the Cartesian way of thinking. Under the influence of Descartes' philosophy, Western medicine grew up along reductionist and dualist lines.

Reductionist methods involve splitting the object of study up into parts, each of which is examined or dealt with separately. Thus medical specialisms developed and continue in the Western tradition. Dualism involves the separation of body and spirit. Thus medicine was the concern of the doctors, and the spirit was the concern of the priesthood, and medicine took no account of spiritual matters. Even psychiatry deals with mental illness largely on a biochemical basis, using drugs to regulate the mental functions.

The idea of energy medicine is foreign to those who practise Western Medicine, and they are inclined to ridicule it because it formed no part of their own training. Some Christians are also inclined to be suspicious of it, associating it with oriental religions. The logical mistake which they make, however, is to confuse chronology with geography and culture. Because the major systems of medicine which first took Vital Energy into account were Chinese and Indian, they classify it as an invention of these civilisations, rather than a timeless phenomenon which was first observed and described by them. Having branded it as an oriental invention, they then associate it with the religions which are practised by many oriental peoples. It is, of course, very difficult to separate the philosophy of a culture from its religion. Every culture and philosophy describes reality as it perceives it. But there is nothing religious about electro-magnetic energy. It is a part of all our lives, whether we embrace Eastern or Western religion or none at all, and it can pose no threat at all to the religious integrity of the Christian.

The fact that some Western Christians think of the Vital Force as oriental and therefore non-Christian is because Western Medicine has developed along materialist and dualist lines. We simply do not expect doctors to concern themselves with such things. It could be regarded as an act of negligence that the Church has colluded with this dualism in medicine for so many years, in spite of Christ's own healing ministry and expectation of those who go out in His name that they should heal(7). To dismiss Vital Force as a non-Christian invention is merely to compound the first error with another. I trust that it is clear from what I have written that the Vital Force, as a form of electro-magnetic energy, is a natural phenomenon and nobody's invention. Christians may safely regard it as a part of God's creation.

Reference must be made to the work of Jacques Benveniste at the INSERM institute in Paris, using "potentized" anti-immunoglobulin E (IgE). The BBC2 programme of 5th July, 1994 in the "Heretics" series described these experiments in detail, as well as the reaction to them of the orthodox scientific community. It is interesting to note that when Benveniste destroyed the electromagnetic energy field of the "potentized" anti-IgE, by placing it inside an activated electromagnetic coil, the anti-IgE no longer had any effect on the blood sample. This would appear to demonstrate clearly that it is the electromagnetic field which is the active factor in causing physical reactions, rather than the chemical composition, certainly when the substance has been diluted beyond the molecular level. (See Appendix I for further comment.)

Appendix II describes some research carried out by the German biophysicist, Fritz-Albert Popp in the early 1980s which demonstrated that the vital functions of living organisms were clearly susceptible to the administration of potentised remedies. What was actually measured was an energy-emission — a manifestation of the electro-magnetic energy field — which correlates closely with many vital functions.

Other research has supported the likelihood that fluids, particularly water, are susceptible to influence by electromagnetic radiation. Georgio Piccardi, director of the Institute for Physical Chemistry in Florence, carried out experiments over a period of ten years, showing that a simple chemical reaction in distilled water varied according to sunspot activity and changes in the Earth's magnetic field(8). These experiments have been repeated and confirmed by a team at Brussels university(9). Further research at Colorado (U.S. Atmospheric Research Centre) confirmed that it is the water which is sensitive to electromagnetic fields in these reactions, rather than other chemical factors(10).

In Homœopathy, except where undiluted tinctures or very low potencies are used, it is the energy-pattern of the prescribed remedy which heals, not the physical substance. For this reason, homœopathic medicines are not washed down to be digested in the stomach, but are dissolved slowly in a clean, fresh mouth or, occasionally, inhaled from the bottle. Their effect is mainly on the energy-fields of the body. A homœopathic prescription does not target germs for destruction, it aims to restore health to the whole person, resulting in the disappearance of the symptoms as they become redundant and of the germs as the body once again becomes able to deal with them.

The fact that microdoses, consisting only of electromagnetic energy-patterns acting on the body's own energy-fields, can restore health gently and safely opens up tremendous possibilities for healing. It means that quite poisonous and unpleasant substances can harmlessly be used to cure those symptoms which they produce in someone who is affected by a gross dose. Above all, it means that those who use them can be liberated from the fear of toxic side-effects and can look forward to effective restoration of their health without risk. Such medicines are compatible with total reverence for the whole patient: body, mind, emotions and spirit.

REFERENCES:

1. Smith C. & Best S.: *Electromagnetic Man*. Dent, London, 1989 (Ch.8 Pt.1)
2. Gordon R.: *Are you Sleeping in a Safe Place?* Dulwich Health Society, 1988.
3. Smith C. & Best S.: *Electromagnetic Man*. Dent, London, 1989.
4. Burr H.S.: *The Fields of Life*. Ballantine, New York, 1972.
5. Hahnemann S.: *Organon of Medicine* § 9-20. (Transl. of 6th Edition: Künzli, Naudé & Pendleton) Gollancz, 1983.
6. Descartes R.: *Discours de la Méthode* (6e Méditation) Garnier, Paris. 1960 (Pg.179)
7. Luke 10: v8. or Mark 16: v18.
8. Piccardi, G. *Exposé introductif, Symposium intern.sur les Rel. Phen. Sol et Terre.* Presses Académiques Européennes. Brussels. 1960.
Piccardi, G. *The Chemical Basis of Medical Climatology.* C.C.Thomas. Springfield, Illinois. 1962.
9. Capel-Boute, C. *Observations sur les tests chimiques de Piccardi.* Presses Académiques Européennes. Brussels. 1960.
10. Fisher, W.; Sturdy, G.; Ryan, M.; Pugh, R. Some laboratory studies of fluctuating phenomena. In Gauquelin, *The Cosmic Clocks.* Peter Owen. London. 1969.

CHAPTER 4

HOMŒOPATHY AND "SCIENTIFIC METHOD"

For many years, Homœopathy has been criticised, or dismissed out of hand, by orthodox science, as having "no rational basis". Whilst this chapter may appear somewhat technical in places, it is important to read it if you wish to appreciate why much of the scientific establishment has such an irretrievable prejudice against Homœopathy. If you do not wish to do so, then please skip the technical bits.

In 1854 there was a cholera epidemic in London. The treatment statistics from the various London hospitals showed that over 50% of cholera patients had died during this epidemic. However, there was one exception. Those for the London Homœopathic Hospital in showed that only 16.4% had died. When the figures were presented to Parliament, those for the London Homœopathic Hospital were left out of the report. The omission was spotted, and the Health Authority was ordered to produce the complete report. When the reason for the omission was sought, the reply was that "if the statistics were made public they would give an unjustified sanction to an empirical practice alike opposed to the maintenance of truth and to the progress of science."

In the 1970's there was a reorganisation of hospital services in Liverpool, and the Department of Homœopathic Medicine was to be moved to the new Royal Liverpool Hospital. A meeting was held to allocate premises in the new hospital, and the homœopathic representative was asked to withdraw. The doctors then agreed in his absence that Homœopathy must be excluded. The minutes noted that they were "horrified to learn that a Homœopathy clinic was suggested." They "insisted unanimously that undergraduates should not be exposed to any unorthodox medicine before qualification; that the very existence of such a clinic in the hospital's prospectus would cause alarm to many doctors and patients; and that the pharmacy should not be asked to supply expensive and dangerous remedies." They also stated that they would not accept any homœopath as a professional colleague in the event of their advice being rejected, and undergraduates would be forbidden to attend the clinic(1).

One wonders what damage they feared would befall the medical undergraduates, and why patients might feel alarmed at the presence of a clinic to which, presumably, they had not been referred. One wonders also what were the "expensive and dangerous remedies" which would not be stocked by a hospital pharmacy anyway, since a considerable number of drugs prescribed in N.H.S. treatment come under this heading, whereas two of the principal characteristics of Homœopathy's remedies are their safety and their inexpensiveness. Tom Ellis, the MP for Wrexham, speaking in the House of Commons in 1977, said that "for sheer blind prejudice and bigotry, crass ignorance and highly questionable ethical behaviour it would be hard to find a better example"(1). But such has been the strength of feeling among orthodox scientists, and many doctors in particular, towards Homœopathy for a long time, although the signs are that this is beginning to change.

From 1982 to 1986, the former West German government commissioned and funded a scientific research project to establish proof of the effectiveness of homœopathic treatment. The project was led by the biophysicist Fritz-Albert Popp at the University of Kaiserslautern, and it concentrated on a phenomenon known as "low-level luminescence" in plant seedlings. This is a form of electro-magnetic energy-emanation found in all living systems, and its intensity correlates closely with all the vital functions of these systems. Popp's research showed that the administration of a potentized remedy, as used in Homœopathy, in a saline solution, had a clear effect on the intensity of the low-level luminescence, which was absent when only the saline solution was added without a remedy. However, early in his report to the West German government (2) he specifically mentions the vigorous opposition to any kind of research which might validate Homœopathy, which he encountered in two German universities and knew of in others. He identified a strong need in many of the scientific hierarchy to preserve the "outsider status" of Homœopathy, and described the lengths to which some professors and other scientists were prepared to go in order to hinder his research and discriminate against students and researchers who took part in it. (See Appendix II for further details of Popp's work.)

In the UK. this longstanding bias against Homœopathy is proving to be a problem where homœopathic colleges seek to have their courses validated for degree-awarding status. Where the proposed degree is to be a science degree, difficulties have been experienced in getting science faculties to take the application seriously. One advantage of this situation could be that homœopathic colleges will look carefully at the content of their courses and re-appraise the extent to which they are training their students to think critically and not merely to swallow undigested quantities of "traditional wisdom". Admittedly the uncritical acceptance of such wisdom has long been a required feature of orthodox medical training, but the latter is officially perceived as being "scientific", whereas Homœopathy is not, which means that it has to strive to be beyond reproach in this respect, however unfair this may appear.

One particular problem, which is perhaps the most difficult obstacle to surmount, is the insistence of the medical establishment on the supremacy of the double-blind crossover placebo-controlled drug trial. Some drugs which had undergone such trials have nonetheless caused large-scale problems for those who took them in good faith. 70 people in the UK. died after taking Opren; 10,000 birth defects are estimated to have been the result of the mothers having taken Thalidomide during pregnancy; 30,000 Japanese were blinded or paralysed after taking Clioquinol. To these sad statistics must be added the figures for drug induced deaths quoted in the Introduction to this book.

The problem so far as Homœopathy is concerned is that such trials are designed on the basis of one drug being prescribed to cure one diagnosed medical condition. The subjects in these trials are all suffering from the same condition, and they are all prescribed the same drug, except for the control group, who receive placebo, an unmedicated pill resembling the medicated one in appearance. However, Homœopathy is not practised in this way. Each patient is appraised individually, and receives the remedy which, in the "picture" of symptoms it has caused in healthy "provers", most closely matches the symptom picture of the patient. Homœopaths, whilst trained to understand the pathological processes which can take place in the human organism, are not primarily concerned with diagnosing a named disease, such as mumps, laryngitis, salmonella poisoning, or whatever. They are concerned with selecting the indicated remedy. Generally, if they talk of diseases, these bear the name of the required remedy: the Belladonna disease, the Thuja disease and so on. Thus out of ten patients diagnosed by a doctor as suffering from disease X, each of the ten might receive a different remedy if prescribed for by a homœopath.

Thus you can see that validating Homœopathy by this method is fraught with problems. It has been used with some success in demonstrating the effectiveness of potentized remedies over placebo (e.g. in the use of potentized pollens for hay fever patients.) Even so, when the results of such trials have been published in the medical press, the cry has sometimes gone up: "It doesn't count, because the medicine was homœopathic!" In order to validate the homœopathic method, a different and more suitable type of research protocol is required, in which, for example, the patients receive the indicated remedy, or else placebo. But even so, there are those in the orthodox camp who seem to take a perverse delight in cornering

Homœopathy in a no-win situation by insisting that in order to be accorded validity it must go through the same trials as Allopathy (but see footnote to page 35 for a ray of hope).

This is the type of thinking to which Popp referred, and reveals a deep-seated anxiety on the part of Allopathy as to what might happen if it allowed Homœopathy to compete on equal terms. No attempt is generally made to address the possibility that Homœopathy might operate on a different basis for which the traditional trial protocol is inappropriate. If the scientific establishment as a whole were as open-minded and unbiased as one would expect true science to be, and less obviously swayed by its self-interested need to ensure that Homœopathy remains an "outsider", homœopaths as a profession might show more interest in taking time out from their healing work to engage in meaningful trials. There are indeed groups of professional homœopaths who are addressing the question of research, but by and large it is not a matter which fires the imagination of the average practitioner.

Scientific trials also require funding. Much medical research is funded by the pharmaceutical industry, and none of that money is likely to become available for research which might result in increased sales of homœopathic remedies and decreased sales of drugs. As the UK. Government is advised on medical matters mainly by the allopathic medical profession, funding is also unlikely to come from that direction in any quantity. Failing the emergence of some wealthy benefactor, large-scale research into Homœopathy is therefore likely to be slow to materialise. But a modest amount of research is being undertaken already by some within the homœopathic medical profession, and it may well be increasingly important for homœopathic practitioners, in addition to proving new remedies, to carry out some kind of audit of the results of their treatments, as even purely statistical evidence is useful, and is easier to use than "anecdotal" evidence of cured cases, which is always abundantly available.

Dr. David Horrobin has identified two types of expert(3). A Type 1 expert is one who knows how to do something useful and important, who is able to solve problems and work constructively. A Type 2 expert's strength, on the other hand, lies in a large volume of knowledge, which he/she is able to access easily.

Psychologist Dr. Ashley Conway, in his article "The Research Game: a view from the field"(4), suggests that modern medical research is dominated by Type 2 experts. Their work is repetitive, with much attention being paid to fine detail. Experiments have a similar structure and tend to minimise the differences between living organisms within the group being studied. Where people are involved, they are dehumanised and their feelings regarding the study are generally irrelevant. Treatment of the "subjects" is standardised, and their behaviour must be as predictable as possible. The type of person who will be attracted to such a work environment is likely to be one who enjoys the security of a structured work pattern and has an overriding concern for attention to detail. Research organisations have adapted to this pattern so as to protect the needs and interests of their members by ensuring that this structure becomes self-maintaining. The more a member receives from it, the greater his or her interest in preserving the status quo.

The consequence of this domination of medical research by Type 2 experts can be easily seen. Over the last 20 years, at 1994 prices, the UK. has spent £2,000 million on medical research. In that time there has been no change in life expectancy and there have been no significant reductions in deaths from the most common forms of cancer or heart disease which could be attributed to public funding of medical research. Talented potential researchers who might come up with innovative ideas for solving medical problems and raising the level of health will not be able to penetrate the research monolith unless they can show aptitude as a Type 2 expert.

If they produce independent results which are at variance with Type 2 thinking, these will be ridiculed or censured by the research establishment, which feels itself threatened by them, and by what Richard Milton has referred to as "The Paradigm Police": often prestigious scientific journals, by which new research reports must be accepted for publication if they are to achieve credibility and approval in the orthodox scientific community(5). Milton quotes the editor of "Nature" who, in 1981, described Prof. Rupert Sheldrake's book "A New Science of Life" as "the best candidate for burning there has been for many years"(6).

By way of example, Conway describes the reaction to a visit

by Erik Peper, an American psychologist, to an international conference on respiratory physiology in Europe. Peper had devised a new method of teaching asthmatics how to adjust their breathing in order to stop asthma attacks. Rather than welcoming Peper and his innovative method, the delegates viewed him as a threat. He was a Type 1 expert (i.e. he was making people better), his solution to the problem of asthma could affect the livelihood of a number of Type 2 asthma experts and pharmaceutical companies, and he interacted with his patients and treated them as individuals. He also embodied a worrying combination of enthusiasm and practical ability, and therefore he needed to be dealt with and cut down to size. The questions which they asked him did not include requests for a demonstration, or details of how quickly the technique worked. Rather they focussed on technical details regarding the type of electrodes used in the biofeedback. This formed a small part of the procedure and was not used with all of the patients. Examining this technicality microscopically they found something to fault, and were able to dismiss his results with obvious relief and get back to the "real" business of research into asthma and other respiratory disorders.

Clearly there is a need for the focus of medical research to shift towards achieving something which is in the interests of patients, rather than producing impressive, introspective, intellectual articles in elitist journals. However, I should like to suggest that one important reason for the non-acceptance of homœopaths by the orthodox medical "paradigm police" is that homœopaths, along with practitioners of many other natural therapies, are Type 1 experts. Every patient who comes into their consulting room is an individual, with a new problem requiring to be solved.

Homœopaths have to be creative problem-solvers by the very nature of their therapy. Any research which de-humanises patients and strips them of their individuality is repugnant to the homœopath. Homœopaths are trained to restore health, not to kill germs and pigeonhole people as "an asthma case" or "an M.E. case". And inevitably the Type 2 expert in the allopathic hierarchy will feel threatened by this and seek to divert attention away from the health-giving achievements of Homœopathy and towards minute technicalities which, in the eyes of Type 2 expertise, will appear to be flaws, and will offer rich opportunities for nit-picking criticism.

In the Middle Ages, the Roman Catholic church instituted the Inquisition in order to remove "heretics" such as the Cathars and others who did not think or worship in the approved way. We may consider that, in their zeal, they departed radically from the spirit of Christ's teaching. People were burnt at the stake and torture was applied to extract recantations. We should not be surprised that, on both sides of the Atlantic, self-appointed influential organisations exist with the aim of rooting out and silencing those of whose scientific ideas they disapprove. Tolerating only one official attitude, they have departed from the open-minded approach which one would expect of true scientists, and they make pronouncements which often proceed from prejudice and are not supported by the results of scientific study.

Christians who encounter such pronouncements about Homœopathy (e.g. that no scientific study has ever demonstrated its effectiveness) should be aware that these are statements of opinion, not fact, and that there is a growing body of hard evidence to the contrary. Those who persist in defending an indefensible position out of blind prejudice are to be pitied, but we cannot respect them for their scientific integrity.

REFERENCES:

1. Inglis, Brian: *Natural Medicine*, P.143-4. Fontana/Collins. Glasgow, 1979.
2. Popp, F.A.: *Bericht an Bonn*. Verlag für Ganzheitsmedizin. Essen. 1986.
3. Horrobin, D. In praise of non-experts. *New Scientist* 24.6.82, pp.842-4.
4. Conway, A.V. The Research Game: a view from the field. *Complementary Medical Research* Vol.3 No.8, pp.29-36, 1988.
5. Milton, R. *Forbidden Science*. Chapt.10. Fourth Estate, London. 1994.
6. *Nature*, Vol.293. pp.245-6. 1981.

OBJECTIONS TO HOMŒOPATHY

(I) ALLOPATHIC VIEWS

A number of books have appeared in recent years which claim to provide a Christian critique of Homœopathy, in some cases along with other natural therapies. I find it significant that of the three which I have read, two [Bopp's, "Homœopathy"(1) and Samuel Pfeifer's, "Healing at any Price?"(2)] come from the pens of allopathic doctors, and one ["New Age Healing"(3)] is written by a team, of whom one is a medic. A perusal of all of these reveals strong elements of allopathic prejudice, although they purport to be written from the Christian perspective.

Thus, although the authors are undoubtedly sincere in their belief that Homœopathy — and other natural therapies — are occult and therefore dangerous for the Christian, it is also possible to perceive a second, parallel agenda, which is the implication that Allopathy is the only right and safe therapy for Christians to use, and the yardstick by which all other therapies are to be judged. Medical arguments in these books proceed from the allopathic, materialist perspective and disregard the different basis on which energy medicines operate. Energy, indeed, is perceived by these authors not as a part of the natural scientific order, open to biophysical investigation, but as something inherently dark and sinister, and likely to contaminate or harm the Christian believer who comes into contact with it.

As we have already seen, relations between Allopathy and Homœopathy, at least in the UK., are becoming more cordial. The B.M.A. has abandoned its dismissive stance towards certain of the Alternative and Complementary therapies, and the passage of the Osteopaths' Bill, and now in 1994 the Chiropractors' Bill, through Parliament has paved the way for legislative recognition and regulation of a number of professions in this field. A review of clinical trials of homœopathic treatment published in 1991 (by Kleijnen et al) reported that 81 out of 105 trials with interpretable findings indicated positive results.

However, old prejudices die hard, and there still remains a hard core within the allopathic profession who were trained to believe that Homœopathy was "unscientific", and that it is their duty to protect their patients from it. Nor should anyone be surprised that someone who has chosen to practise a particular medical modality, and has invested several years of their life in training for this, regards it as the "best" available therapy. After all, if one ceases to believe this, the intellectually honest thing to do is to quit, as Hahnemann did, and seek a better way.

Christians who read critiques of alternative therapies written by doctors should therefore be aware of the possibility of bias on the part of the authors. Such bias is understandable if it is declared, but what is disturbing is that in some cases it is cloaked in religious terms, and that the authors speak authoritatively about therapies other than their own from an uninformed, prejudiced and sometimes arrogant point of view, ridiculing ideas which they have first misrepresented. I should like to give some examples of what I mean.

If we read Bopp's booklet, we find that he quotes "A Practical Guide to Homœopathy", by one J. Hodler as recommending the use of Pyrogen 7C (i.e. in the 7th centesimal potency) in septicæmia. His comment: "The condition of septicæmia is a serious one and may terminate in death should immediate, appropriate, *antibiotic* treatment not be administered." (My emphasis.) This is an allopathic statement. In Allopathy the use of antibiotics would be appropriate. But

Bopp clearly dismisses the possibility that Pyrogen would also work, within a homœopathic context, and clearly considers that Homœopathy is useless in "serious conditions". Had he had the opportunity of observing a potentially fatal post-partum hæmorrhage cease within less than a minute of taking the "appropriate" homœopathic remedy, or the near-miraculous recovery of a patient in apparent terminal collapse when given Carbo vegetabilis, I hope he would have reconsidered his opinion(4). But his bland assumption that Homœopathy is ineffective is typical of allopathic prejudice, and betrays a regrettable lack of investigation into the therapy which he is criticising. Had he investigated it with an open mind before putting pen to paper, it is possible that his booklet might never have been written, since many before him who have set out to discredit Homœopathy and have really taken the trouble to look into it honestly have emerged from the process as convinced homœopaths.

"The serious treatment of an illness," he continues, "is undertaken by means of drugs, the primary action and secondary effects of which are known, and sometimes by surgical intervention. Present-day medicine, as taught in the universities, speaks only very little about Homœopathy. Its basic literature, as well as the scientific periodicals, do not mention it." Whilst effortless superiority emanates from every line of the above, it is clearly written from an uninformed position, implying as it does that the effects of homœopathic remedies are not known, and that homœopathic treatment is not "serious".

In fact, the action and effects of the remedies used in Homœopathy are very precisely known from the provings, and are set out in painstaking detail in the Materia Medicas and Repertories which are the basic reference tools of the homœopath. Others might argue that his initial statement is correct, since homœopathic treatment is directed at people, not illnesses. However, I doubt that this is what he had in mind. His following assertions, like a number of other statements in his booklet, are quite incorrect regarding the status quo in the United Kingdom, and the blame for this should be borne by careless editing.

The University of Glasgow Medical School has introduced a Homœopathy option as part of its degree course for intending doctors, and in France the University of Bordeaux has a thorough post-graduate programme of homœopathic studies. Scientific periodicals increasingly carry reports of studies involving potentized remedies†. Nor does the fact that reference is constantly made to Hahnemann's "Organ" (rather than Organon) inspire great confidence in the translator's and editor's knowledge of their subject!

Dr. Pfeifer, too, displays a massive lack of appreciation of homœopathic methodology in his chapter on Homœopathy. With scarcely concealed incredulity he invites his reader to ridicule the fine differentiation of various fears, as described in "How to find the proper Remedy", by C.F. Gauss. "Thus he lists not fewer that (sic) 24 forms of fear, every form requiring a different medication. Anxiety before giving birth to a child is treated with the remedy *Cimicifuga* in a potentiation (sic) of 30X, 'fear that something might come out of a corner' with *Phosphor* 6X (sic), fear of being touched, combined with severe sadness and a miserable mood requires *Antimonium crudum*, and 'fear of pointed objects,(knives, forks and the like)' is treated with *Strophanthus gratus* 6X, the extract being made from an African plant containing heart-active substances."

Not only does Pfeifer overlook the fact that a homœopath would seldom prescribe solely on such single symptoms, since it is the whole person who is being treated, rather than the illness, but he clearly fails to appreciate the whole point of the differentiation: that different symptoms are produced in the provings of different substances, and only the substance which has caused the symptoms in the healthy prover can bring about healing in the patient whose disease is characterised by those same symptoms.

---

† In 1994 the American medical journal Pediatrics published a research report on the homœopathic treatment of acute childhood diarrhœa in Nicaragua. About 5 million children die every year from this condition, especially in less developed countries. The treatment group received a variety of homœopathic medicines, while the control group received a placebo. The treatment group recovered 15-25% more quickly than the control group. The journal concluded that this study "introduces an effective, low-cost treatment for this widespread condition". Bopp was, of course, writing some years before this.

Sir John Weir said, in a paper given to the Royal Society of Medicine in 1933: "Hahnemann showed that Homœopathy is absolutely inconceivable without the most precise individuation. The names of diseases should never influence the physician, who has to judge and cure diseases not by name, but by the signs and symptoms of each individual patient. Since diseases can only express their need for relief by symptoms, the totality of symptoms observed in each individual case of disease can be the only indication to guide in the choice of the remedy. Hahnemann knew no disease, only sick persons."

Pfeifer also makes a fundamental error in assuming that homœopathic remedies are prescribed on the basis of a diagnosed mineral deficiency, and in confusing biochemic tissue salts (developed by Schüssler) with constitutional remedies. Schüssler's system of biochemic tissue salts is admittedly based on the idea that a deficiency of certain mineral salts which occur naturally in the body leads to ill-health. His twelve tissue salts are prescribed on a symptomatic basis, and normally taken in a 6X potency.

However, constitutional homœopathic prescribing is emphatically not undertaken on the basis of deficiencies of substances needed by the body. It is the result of a careful matching of the patient's symptoms on all levels to the most similar constellation of symptoms which result from the proving of a remedy. One may conceive of a patient with a deficiency of calcium, or even of some essential trace element, but is it likely that a patient would suffer from a deficiency of Tarantula spider or snake poison, of Deadly Nightshade or Hemlock? On what basis would such frequently life-saving prescriptions be made, if deficiency were the yardstick?

Having paraded his ignorance of homœopathic principles in this way, Pfeifer then compounds it by introducing the contentious issue of immunisation, describing it as "an accepted method of healing like with like". It is of course nothing of the kind. To start with, immunisation is not a method of healing; its use is preventive. One does not immunise someone to cure them of an illness from which they are suffering. One hopes to prevent them from contracting the illness, and he even goes on to say as much.

He appears to be saying that homœopaths use the analogy

of immunisation to support Homœopathy. Whilst there may be some homœopathic doctors who employ this analogy, I am certainly not aware of any professional homœopaths who use it, or would want to be associated with it. Hahnemann was initially interested in vaccination, but eventually rejected it. Pfeifer rightly points out that immunisation does not operate in the same way as Homœopathy.

However, having put an argument into the mouths of the homœopaths, he then goes on to say: "This example shows......how scientific discoveries are taken out of context to support bizarre claims." He then further argues that the success of Homœopathy is due to the placebo effect, again totally disregarding the evidence — provided by its successful use in veterinary practice — that this cannot possibly be the case. How could a herd of cows drinking water from a trough to which a few drops of a homœopathic remedy had been added be cured of mastitis as a result of placebo effect?(5)

Sadly it has to be pointed out that Pfeifer has thrown up the opportunity of providing a reasoned, informed and in-depth critique of homœopathic philosophy and practice in favour of misrepresentation and ridicule. He picks out quotations, sometimes from obscure books, to give an impression which fits in with his thesis that Homœopathy is bizarre, irrational, and has its roots in Eastern mysticism. And above all he is approaching it from an allopathic, materialist point of view.

Firstly he completely discounts the scientific status of electromagnetic energy, which I have discussed elsewhere, and secondly his materialistic approach to medicine limits his understanding of healing to "organic effects".

Homœopaths do not set out to create organic effects. Their remedies are prescribed for the purpose of restoring health in the patient. No assumptions are made as to whether the restoration of health is an organic process; indeed it is generally considered to be a question of restoring the resonance of the patient's electromagnetic energy fields. Once this is achieved, then organic healing should be just one consequence, assuming that the focus of the disease was on the organic level. It is just as likely that it may have been on the emotional or mental level, in which case organic effects may not be evident, but we have to assume that for Pfeifer "disease" comprises solely of malfunctioning physical organs, and "health" comprises solely of properly functioning organs. This is in stark contrast to the W.H.O. declaration at Alma Ata in 1978, when health was defined as follows: "Health is a state of complete physical, mental and social well-being; it is not merely the absence of infirmity or disease,.......it is a fundamental human right." To this we might add the definition given by Dr. Leslie Weatherhead in 1951 in "Psychology, Religion and Healing"(6). "Health is a complete and successful functioning of the human being, in harmonious relationship with every part, and with the relevant environment." Viewed against such a panoramic background, an understanding of health such as Pfeifer's seems depressingly impoverished. Christians deserve better than this. Indeed, so do all patients.

Also glaringly obvious in Pfeifer's argument is his allopathic blind-spot, which he disguises in gratuitous religious language. Having stated that the success of homœopathic treatment is due to the placebo effect, he admits that this may have some value insofar as it saves people from taking more dangerous and habit-forming drugs. Then comes a most extraordinary statement: "But Christians have to ask themselves: why do we believe so much in homœopathic pills and tinctures and have so little trust in the caring provision of our Lord? There is a great danger in giving all the honour to the remedy instead of to God who created our bodies. Some who claim that God has provided the homœopathic remedies see no problem there. Yet how can we readily accept that these remedies are from Him?"

Notice how he introduces a religious smoke-screen here, in the form of a completely artificial and false alternative. Since Homœopathy is clearly not placebo effect, working as it does on animals and unconscious people, cure is not a question of believing in the remedies, in any case. But to suggest that there is a choice for the Christian between believing either in homœopathic remedies or in God is a totally false and misleading argument. What about those Christians who rely upon insulin to control their diabetes, or upon steroids to control their asthmatic attacks? Are they also being unfaithful and disloyal to God? Presumably to Pfeifer it is obvious that such medicines are from God. And presumably it is only his allopathic blind-spot which prevents him from accepting that any medicines may be a gift of God, not just allopathic ones. What is there to prevent a cured homœopathic patient from giving thanks to God for his or her recovery or for the remedy or the skill of the practitioner in working it out? Nothing. And yet Pfeifer exploits the piety of his mainly Christian readership, and insults their intelligence, by suggesting that a belief in homœopathic remedies represents disloyalty to God. This is sheer hypocrisy: allopathic prejudice dressed up in Christian words, and it is this kind of thing against which Christians should be on their guard if they are seeking unbiased, reliable advice on Homœopathy or any other natural therapy.

Allopathic prejudice also shows through in "New Age Medicine" by Reisser, Reisser and Weldon. The meaning of the term :"Natural Medicine" is fudged quite early on in the book, when we read: "A positive by-product of the holistic health movement may be that of steering people away from a drug-oriented approach to life, but a less desirable result is the propagation of a peculiar logic which states that anything done without medications and surgery is by definition 'natural'. Healing methods which have no basis in reality or common sense, which openly defy well-established principles of biology and which in some cases *tamper with dangerous realms of the occult* (my emphasis), have acquired respectability by being referred to as natural.........When a serious disease can be readily treated with medications or surgery, a patient's refusal to follow any approach other than a 'natural' one might lead to a needless catastrophe. Most oncologists have at least one case of a curable tumor (sic) which became hopelessly widespread while the patient pursued what seemed to be a more natural cure."

Whether the authors actually believe this, or whether they are deliberately trying to create confusion in order to influence their readership, the result is the latter. Natural medicine has nothing to do with the presence or absence of medication; the criterion is whether or not the therapy assists the body's innate tendency to heal itself. Thus Herbal Medicine (Phytotherapy) and Homœopathy both involve medication, but work in partnership with the human organism, rather than against it as would be the case with allopathic drugs.

The authors do not state which healing methods "have no basis in reality or common sense", nor do they state which "well-established principles of biology" are "openly defied" (what associations that phrase must conjure up for the average law-abiding Christian citizen!), and the juxtaposition of the words "occult" and "dangerous" is undoubtedly not accidental. It seems to be assumed that if a serious disease can be readily treated by (allopathic) medication or surgery, these are automatically the logical first choice, especially in view of the scary aside about oncologists and their cases of curable tumours becoming incurable. (Are we to assume that cancer patients never die under allopathic treatment?) But this is the type of suggestion which is common in such books and is designed to convey the misinformation that Allopathy is safe, whilst other therapies are fraught with hidden dangers which are only hinted at and remain cloaked in an aura of sinister darkness. Clearly the authors are unaware of the revulsion which many people feel towards reductionist medicine and the suppositions which it makes about the human being, making it anything but the obvious first choice in cases of disease, serious or otherwise.

Earlier in the opening chapter of that book, a picture is painted of medicine moving out of a shadowy world of primitive and supernatural methods into the dawn of technological and scientific medicine. It is fairly stated that the encroachment of technology into the realm of medicine needs to be limited because we are dealing with human beings rather than misbehaving cell-cultures. Reference is made to many health disorders remaining "complex mysteries, understood only in the crudest sense", although they do not explore the possibility that this might be because science limits itself to crude, physical methods.

The question of evaluation is also a problem for the authors of this book "Normally" they say, (meaning: in Allopathic method) "a therapy is evaluated by comparing a group of patients which is treated with a similar group which is not...... But how can you compare 'treatment' and 'non-treatment' groups when disease categories are meaningless and when no two patients can be treated in the same way? How can the effects of a treatment even be measured when you cannot use the patient's physical status as a guide to your progress?"

No doubt these questions are rhetorical and the implied answer is: "You cannot". However, the asking of such questions displays an inability to think laterally. Another possible answer to the first question is that you use a method which is appropriate to the therapy being evaluated, rather than to Allopathy. Thus, as suggested in Chapter 4, a suitable method might be to have a treatment group whose members were all suffering from the same allopathically diagnosed condition, but who received their homœopathically indicated remedy, rather than the same blanket prescription. The non-treatment or control group would receive placebo (see footnote to page 35).

The second question has an answer which is supplied by homœopathic methodology, since homœopaths have their own criteria for assessing the progress of the patient and the success or otherwise of a prescription (see Chapter 1). The patient's physical status may well play a part in the assessment, but his or her emotional and mental status and level of vitality are equally important factors, which are unfortunately discounted by Allopathy. This again suggests that the judgments in this book are being made from an allopathic viewpoint.

Again, in the following paragraph, the authors claim that the material of Homœopathy is resistant to revision based on contrary evidence. "If the patient improves, the treatment worked. If he or she worsens, the treatment is merely affecting the way in which the inner disturbance is 'ventilating' itself. Any result can be explained by the theory. (In some cases this assumption could be disastrous. If signs of critical illness are misinterpreted as another 'ventilation', a patient could be ushered into a premature grave.)"

Surely the theory would be inadequate if it were not capable of explaining any results produced by the treatment; but the above statement is a caricature. In the first place, any trained homœopath is well aware of Hering's Law of Cure, which provides precise criteria for assessing a patient's progress under treatment. Such criteria as "improves" or "worsens" are too simplistic. A patient's original physical symptoms may be much better after taking a homœopathic remedy, but if the patient is mentally or emotionally in a worse state, or if physical symptoms arise which show that the patient is adversely affected on a deeper physical level, then the practitioner knows that the treatment has been suppressive and the patient is less healthy. The treatment must therefore be antidoted and a fresh start made. On the other hand, the original physical symptoms might be aggravated, but the patient is feeling energised, positive and more able to cope with everyday stress. In such a case healing is taking place, and the physical symptoms will improve in the course of time.

In the second place, a professionally trained homœopath will have studied enough human sciences to recognise signs of critical illness. It is unfortunately common among allopaths, even those who are sympathetic to natural therapies, to show fear regarding the supposed lack of ability of natural health practitioners to recognise or diagnose life-threatening conditions. It is true that allopaths' primary training is in the diagnosis of illnesses. It is likewise true that natural health practitioners' primary training is in understanding the nature of health and disease. One obvious solution would be the creation of more group practices, where both types of medicine could work alongside each other in partnership, enabling expertise to be shared and pooled for the ultimate benefit of the patient.

Towards the end of this book, the authors give a list of "caveats" for those who are seeking alternative treatments. Whilst some of these are sound common sense, there are others which display a strong degree of allopathic bias. For example, the list begins with "Beware of therapies which claim to manipulate 'invisible energy'." This is followed by a passage which reiterates one of the book's main arguments: that energy can only be supernatural or illusory. Clearly they see no place for electromagnetic energy which is a part of the natural scientific order of things, certainly not within medicine. "Christian therapists may claim that the invisible energies they purport to influence are part of God's creation, but in doing so they betray a misinformed notion of the scope of the natural realm. They are in fact toying either with the supernatural or an illusion."

Thus the medical position of this book is made abundantly clear: it is based fairly and squarely on Cartesian reductionism, and wilfully closes its eyes to all recent scientific studies which demonstrate the role of electromagnetic energy in basic human functions and existence. It is in fact the authors who are misinformed regarding the scope of the natural realm, in either not keeping up to date with current scientific work, or deliberately disregarding it because it does not fit their hypothesis.

However, worse is to come. "Head for the exit immediately when someone claims that the medical establishment is evil or satanic, that the government or the A.M.A. are persecuting them or that other doctors are intent on stealing their discovery."

Clearly such a person could be suffering from delusions of persecution; however, in the case of the A.M.A., history suggests that this might be anything but a delusion. The A.M.A. (American Medical Association) was founded to defend the interests of the allopathic system of medicine and its practitioners in the U.S.A., chiefly against Homœopathy. However, along the way it has acquired an invidious reputation for hounding many an innovative alternative practitioner out of practice or out of the country. Its position is patently biased in favour of allopathic practice and any natural practitioner in the USA could reasonably expect to fall foul of it. I have to be suspicious, too, of any organisation which effectively states that it can do no wrong.

When faced with the effects of suppressive medicine, it is surprising that more natural practitioners do not use the word "evil"; however, generally they recognise that allopaths on the whole are sincere, well-intentioned professionals who do the best they can with the inadequate system at their disposal. I suspect that the reason for this curious sensitivity on the part of the allopathic authors of this book towards being dubbed "evil" or "satanic" lies in their own tendency to do precisely that to other equally well-intentioned health professionals, or the modalities which they practise! One wonders why allopaths should be allowed the monopoly of this type of smear.

"Beware of therapies which rely heavily on altered states of consciousness", the authors caution, "Scripture puts no premium whatsoever on altered states, but assumes that we will interact with our creator using an alert, conscious mind." Whilst proscribing hypnotherapy and the use of transcendental meditation, this of course also precludes the medical use of narcotics, anæsthetics and most of the drugs used in psychiatric medicine. I wonder why the latter were not mentioned.

To sum up, whilst many allopaths are becoming increasingly interested in natural therapies, or even practising them to varying extents, there remains an inbuilt prejudice on the part of many others towards Homœopathy, which they regard as "unscientific" or "irrational". The reason for this prejudice lies largely in the facts that it is an energy medicine, and that Allopathy deals only with tangible, physical matters and has no place in its philosophy for biophysical energy, which is intangible. Those critiques of Homœopathy which claim to speak from a Christian viewpoint come mainly from within the allopathic profession, and in my experience proceed from a position of assumed allopathic medical superiority coupled with a misunderstanding or fear of the nature of vital energy. This leads them to use the label "occult", which is addressed in our next chapter.

REFERENCES:

1. Bopp, H.J. *Homœopathy*. (Transl. Kilgore, M.) Great Joy Publications. Carryduff, Belfast. 2nd edition. 1985.

2. Pfeifer, S. *Healing at any Price*. Word (UK) Ltd., Milton Keynes. 1988 (Engl. edition) (Original German edition, 1980)

3. Reisser, P.C., Reisser, T.K. & Weldon J. *New Age Medicine*. Inter Varsity Press, Illinois. 1987.

4. For an example of such a Carbo vegetabilis cure, see: Tyler M.L.: *Homœopathic Drug Pictures* (3rd edition) Pp. 207-8. Health Science Press, Holsworthy. 1952.

5. Day, C. *The Homœopathic Treatment of Beef and Dairy Cattle*, Beaconsfield: Beaconsfield Publishers, 1995. (P. 120).

6. Weatherhead, L. Psychology, *Religion and Healing*. Hodder & Stoughton, London. 1951.

OBJECTIONS TO HOMŒOPATHY

(II) CHRISTIAN VIEWS

A number of Christian writers, mostly with a background in allopathic medicine, have classified Homœopathy, and indeed other complementary and alternative medical modalities, as being "occult". The root meaning of this word is "hidden", and it is generally used to refer to activities which have some basis in sorcery or involve the activity of demonic spirits. These activities generally involve the acquisition of knowledge which is not freely available to human research, reason or speculation, or which is the result of revelation which is supernatural but not from God. It may involve some kind of ritual designed either to acquire hidden knowledge or to achieve power over other beings which comes from a source other than God. The term "sorcery" is sometimes employed as a more specific description of such activities(1a).

I have tried hard to see some way in which the medical discipline of Homœopathy might fall under any of the above criteria, and so far I have failed to do so. The underlying theory, the "Law of Similars", which underpins this therapy is, as we have seen, an ancient natural law dating at least from the time of

Hippocrates. The fact that substances which cause symptoms in the healthy can heal the same symptoms in the sick is a demonstrable and observable fact which does not require any occult knowledge. The Potentization principle, likewise, appears to have arisen from an astute observation by Hahnemann, while his insistence on carefully measured serial dilutions at each stage of potentization proceeded from his insistence on proper scientific method. He was, after all, a noted chemist of his time. Whilst the cynical observer might describe the procedures of homœopathic pharmacy as a "ritual", this would be no more true than it would be of some procedures in orthodox scientific method, and there is in them no intent of acquiring hidden knowledge or achieving power over others; the sole purpose is to heal the sick. Indeed I know of a number of homœopathic practitioners who make it their express aim to empower their patients as much as possible to be in charge of their own health and healing whereas the perception of many patients within orthodox medicine is of their doctor as being an "authority figure". If there is power over others, it would seem to be vested at least as much in Allopathy as in Homœopathy, if not more so.

At least one Christian writer critical of Homœopathy has suggested that the process of potentization itself charges the remedies with "occult power". However, to be fair, this view is not shared by all such critics, and it is charitable to attribute this to a misunderstanding of the process and an ignorance of the properties of electromagnetic energy. Certainly there seems to be little if any biblical evidence for the charging of physical objects or substances with demonic power(1b). Some physicists have accepted the potentization process as a simple transfer of kinetic energy as a result of the succussion or trituration, and there seems to be no particular reason for the assumption that the energy is in any way occult, demonic, sinister or harmful.

Nor does potentization have anything to do with the acquisition of power. Rather, it may be seen as the releasing or amplification of existing latent energy. It is interesting that two of the most powerful medicines in homœopathic use are medicinally inert in their crude form and are only of medicinal use when potentized. One of these is *Lycopodium*, the spores of the Club Moss plant: a medicine of very wide use in treating patients of a particular constitutional type. The other is *Carbo vegetabilis* — wood charcoal — which has brought many patients back from the brink of the grave when the light of life was all but extinguished. Many such responses to a correctly selected homœopathic remedy could be — and sometimes are — jokingly described as "magic". However, this is a trivialisation of the serious work of healing. The magician's role is to entertain and impress, some would say to deceive. The homœopath's work is to stimulate the organism's natural self-healing tendency, by matching the patient's symptoms in every possible respect to the substance which has produced the most similar symptom-pattern in the healthy when "proved" by them, and by administering a safe preparation of that substance.

Another charge levelled by those who accuse Homœopathy of being occult is that some practitioners make use of pendulums and dowse for their remedies. (Indeed the impression given by one such writer is that this is the general practice.) This raises an important and interesting issue, which is generalisation from the particular. The author in question, Dr. H.J. Bopp of Neuchâtel, Switzerland(2), refers to "a very high percentage of homœopaths" who work with the pendulum, and it appears that there may be a number of folk-healers in Switzerland who select their remedies by dowsing. However, it is also true to say that an allopathic doctor or a herbalist could likewise use this method to diagnose or to select medicines. This would not make dowsing an integral part of the therapy itself. It is questionable logic to say that, because some people cycle to work, the only way of getting to work is by bicycle.

The pendulum was once described to me by someone who uses one, as "an extension of the user's intuition." Intuition can be of use in many spheres of human activity. However, I can state authoritatively that the selection of remedies by pendulum is not taught as any part of homœopathic practice by the dozen or so colleges recognised by the British homœopathic profession, nor does it appear in the current Core Curriculum of homœopathic professional studies published by the European Council for Classical Homœopathy. This is for the guidance of professional training in those European countries where homœopathic practice is not restricted to those with an allopathic training. Nor have I encountered any visiting lecturers in

Homœopathy from India, Greece, or South American countries who have advocated the use of the pendulum. Professional homœopaths are taught to select their remedies on the basis of careful observation and questioning of the patient. If anyone chooses to use the pendulum for remedy-selection, or any other purpose, it is a private and personal choice of their own, and no part of the methodology of Homœopathy. Were I convinced that Switzerland is populated by homœopathic gnomes living in caves and swinging pendulums all day, then I might concede that no-one should seek homœopathic treatment in Switzerland. However, from reading an international homœopathic journal published in that country until 1996 ("Homœopathic Links"), it is clear that reputable homœopathic practice is well established there.

Bopp quotes Hosea 4:12-14 as evidence of biblical disapproval of the pendulum. I have to say that I have looked up this passage in six different English translations of the Bible, including the Authorized, and in none of them does the word "pendulum" appear. (The others are the Revised, the Revised Standard, the Jerusalem, the New English and the Good News.) They all render the word in question as "staff", "rod", "fetish", or "stick". One German version also gave "Stab" rather than "Pendel", so I wonder whether there is actually any biblical pronouncement at all on the use of the pendulum. The passage in question from Hosea is concerned with matters of idolatry and temple prostitution, referring possibly to the tree-cult which was practiced by some ancient Semitic peoples. Oaks and terebinths were revered as sacred trees, oracles were sought from them, and near them sacrifices were offered and sacred prostitution was practised. Hosea is urging the Israelites to avoid such practices because of their association with heathen Canaanite worship. They are also condemned in Deuteronomy (e.g. Ch.12:2.) The other quotations which Bopp uses to support his anti-Homœopathy argument are all taken from Leviticus and refer to practices which are unrelated to Homœopathy as a therapy.

There is another school of thought, represented for example in the book "New Age Medicine" by Reisser, Reisser and Weldon, which seeks to lump Homœopathy together with all the esoteric activities which come under the heading of the "New Age". Such books tend to dismiss New Age thinking and activities as being of oriental or mystical origin, and therefore non-Christian and dangerous for Christians, since they entice the believer away from Jesus Christ. The assumption seems to be that any Christian seeking treatment with a therapy which has Eastern connections will become sullied in some way or converted to an oriental religion. This is as absurd as claiming that a Buddhist who was treated in an N.H.S. hospital would be converted to Christianity by having an endoscopy or taking painkillers.The characteristics of a system of medicine may reflect aspects of the civilisation in which it first appeared, but that system of medicine is quite distinct from the civilisation, philosophy and religion of its country of origin.

The authors of "New Age Medicine" not only write from a position of allopathic supremacy, but they appear to be at pains to fudge the boundary between holistic medicine and the New Age movement. "Furthermore, in the holistic health movement, wellness has a tendency to be equated with enlightenment as understood in Eastern mysticism — involving altered states of consciousness in which psychic or supernatural experiences may occur." Whilst this may be true of some New Age prac-tices, it is of course totally misleading to make such assertions, since the precept under discussion — that health is more than the absence of disease — was propounded by the World Health Organization back in 1978 at Alma Ata, and not by any New Age cult.

In reading such books, we need to be aware of the current trend in the United States among right-wing Christian groups to censor any material apparently connected with the New Age, and to dismiss it all as satanic. This campaign is being waged with a fanaticism redolent of the McCarthyite purges of Communist thinkers and sympathisers, and it is illustrative of the excesses and naïveté of the movement that pictures of Santa Claus have been banned from schools, and the teachers who put them up have been branded as "satanists", because the name "Santa" is an anagram of "Satan"!

I believe it is somewhat arrogant to dismiss the entire wisdom of the oriental culture as primitive, dangerous and occult. Certainly there may be some aspects of New Age think-ing which are incompatible with Christian belief. The authors of "New Age Medicine" go so far as to assert a fundamental split between New Age and Christian "theologies" although, maybe intentionally, they create confusion by referring to the "spiritual outlook of holistic health" rather than that of the New Age movement. It cannot be reiterated too strongly that holistic therapies are not the same thing as the New Age movement, and that in order to practise Homœopathy or any other natural therapy, as with Allopathy, it is quite unnecessary to embrace New Age ideology, or indeed any ideology at all. However, the Christian Church should perhaps be asking itself why so many Western people in recent years have turned to Eastern culture and spiritual practices. What are they seeking and why could they not find it in the Western Christian tradition? It seems to me that the Church should at least consider the possibility that it is paying the price for its connivance at, and tacit acceptance of, dualism. (This is the separation of medical and spiritual matters, making the doctors responsible for the former and the clergy responsible for the latter.) Healing has by and large become the province of doctors; doctors, moreover, of allopathic medicine, and the Church has neglected the command of Christ to His followers to go out and heal. I am reminded of J. Cameron Peddie's complaint in his book "The Forgotten Talent"(3), that members of his Glasgow congregation were going to Spiritualist mediums for healing, because there was no-one in the Church to whom they could turn. (His solution to this problem was to undertake a long period of strict spiritual discipline, after which he was granted the gift of healing by laying-on of hands.)

In seeking to condemn the New Age movement because of perceived conflict between its theological belief system and that of Christianity, evangelical Christians appear to have lost sight of the fundamental characteristics of the New (or Aquarian) Age. Basically the New Age rejects such qualities as violence and materialism and seeks a way of life characterised by gentleness and spirituality — surely highly compatible with Christianity, though not with allopathic medicine. A Christian order, the Michael Order, actually exists, which seeks to reconcile New Age and Christian thinking. By rejecting the New Age summarily, perhaps mainly on the basis of some of its more superficial characteristics, evangelicals risk throwing out the baby with the bathwater.

If large numbers of people in the so-called "New Age" movement prefer to use alternative or complementary therapies, it is because they seek a way of life in which the spiritual dimension is fully integrated, and they find the dualistic orientation of Allopathy spiritually impoverished and barren. The Church has concerned itself with the souls, rather than the bodies, of its members. An exception may be found in the case of medical missionaries, but they of course have been overwhelmingly allopathic, with the exception of those trained at the Missionary School of Medicine (now known as Medical Service Ministries). This outstanding organization has been training missionaries in Homœopathy for 90 years, its teachers have all been practising Christians who are also highly qualified in Homœopathy, and its firm belief is that Homœopathy is spiritually neutral.

This statement may also require clarification. Homœopathy, in common with other holistic therapies, recognises the spiritual dimension of human beings. This does not necessarily make it a "spiritual therapy" in the religious sense, and it has no religious alignment. Individual practitioners of any therapy may be Christians, or adherents of any other religion, or of none. Christian Allopaths and Christian Homœopaths may both pray over their pills, once they have selected them according to the rules of their respective medical disciplines. This is a ritual, but would not make either of them sorcerors. Nor would praying prior to selection of the medication; although non-Christian practitioners might view the practice with suspicion, and it is not a necessary part of the remedy selection or of the therapy itself; rather it is a part of the Christian way of life, like saying Grace before meals. A Christian may eat without saying Grace, but the act of eating becomes less significant or meaningful.

The point is that Homœopathy was established as a medical discipline long before the New Age arrived. Having created an association in their readers' minds by including Homœopathy in a book on New Age Medicine, the authors then concede that, in its original form Homœopathy bore some resemblance to biblical theology, referring to Hahnemann's thinking that chronic disease might be explained by an inherited taint which had some similarity with original sin. Hahnemann, indeed, was described by one of his biographers, Grossinger, as a "puritanical Christian" all of his life.

Unable to address this fact further, they then shift the direction of their argument by attacking Homœopathy as "fundamentally anti-scientific". This of course is quite a different issue and has to do with a scientific blind-spot on the part of the authors, or else an inadequate understanding of Homœopathy's scientific basis. It is discussed more fully elsewhere, and is neither a Christian nor a spiritual issue. It only serves to underscore the allopathic bias of the authors.

Another argument which is sometimes used to prejudice Christian readers against Homœopathy is the fact that some practitioners use Astrology. The same reply applies here as was discussed at some length above with regard to pendulums and prayer. The use of Astrology is a private and personal matter. Some people find it a useful tool in their understanding of human behaviour. Homœopaths have to study their patients' behaviour in some detail in order to arrive at a holistic remedy-diagnosis. Some who have a knowledge of Astrology may choose to use it to assist them in this. This does not mean that Astrology is any part of Homœopathic method or practice per se, and the majority of Homœopaths manage to practise perfectly well without it.

It has also been asserted that Hahnemann was a Freemason, which might make him a non-Christian, and therefore Christians should have nothing to do with the system of medicine which he founded. Leaving aside the controversial contemporary question of the compatibility of Freemasonry and Christianity, on which I have an open mind, the above statement shows an ignorance of the fact that the Lodge had quite different characteristics in the time of Hahnemann from those which it has today. In those days to become a Freemason was more or less obligatory for intellectuals and original thinkers, and Hahnemann was certainly both of those. People who believe that by discrediting the inventor of a particular system of medicine they can discredit the whole system, are playing games with logic. In the case of Hahnemann, we are in any case not dealing with the "inventor" of Homœopathy. The therapeutic principle had been in existence for centuries, as we have seen already, and Hahnemann's contribution was to organise it into a systematic and workable therapy.

The criticism has also been voiced that if tablets of two or more different high-potency remedies from the same pharmacy are subjected to chemical laboratory analysis, their composition is found to be exactly the same. Therefore, the argument runs, their sale as different substances is fraudulent, and any effect they have must be either placebo effect or possibly of a magical or occult nature.

Thorwald Dethlefsen has provided an inspired reply to this argument(4). Chemical laboratory analysis of two different cassette tapes from the same manufacturer will likewise yield identical results. Nothing in this type of analysis will reveal that one of the tapes carried a recording of Reggae music and the other a recording of Chopin's Nocturnes. Chemical analysis is concerned with only one aspect of what it investigates: the physical/material aspect. There is more to both cassette tapes and to potentized remedies than the purely physical. Both are vehicles for a message. Those who investigate phenomena of any kind must be careful to select the appropriate method. If they deliberately select an inappropriate method, which is likely to provide the outcome in which they have a vested interest, their impartiality and open-mindedness, along with the validity of their investigation, must be called in question.

To sum up, then: Homœopathy, whilst recognising the spiritual dimension of human beings, is not a "spiritual" activity in the religious sense of the word. No worship of any being or entity is involved in its practice, nor does it require any rituals which correspond to the definitions of occultism or sorcery. It is based on a scientific law, and the careful observation of cause and effect. The medication which it prescribes has been prepared using a pharmaceutical and biophysical procedure (see Appendix I), which renders the substance free of toxic effects whilst making it the vehicle of an electro-magnetic energy frequency pattern. In the course of the homœopathic case-taking this pattern has been matched to the disease-producing disturbance in the patient's own energy-field, as indicated by the symptoms. There is nothing in any of this which could be suspected of sorcery or occultism, once its scientific mechanism is understood.

Samuel Pfeifer, in his book "Healing at any Price?"(5) , says: "I would issue a special warning against all remedies beyond a potency of 6X to 12X, as there is no other explanation for their success than an occult one, or a placebo effect." This statement sounds authoritative but is, of course, totally inaccurate and misinformed. Electromagnetic energy provides a perfectly feasible and logical non-occult and non-supernatural explanation and, as we have seen, the fact that a liquid can retain a memory of a substance once dissolved in it even after dilution beyond the molecular level has been demonstrated and replicated under laboratory conditions, to the consternation of the scientific establishment(6).

There is also ample evidence that all homœopathic cures cannot be attributed to the placebo effect. These words of Dr. Pfeifer, then, are the words of a man whose understanding of healing is severely limited to the purely material, organic level, and who seeks to play upon the fears of superstitious people in order to prejudice them against a system of medicine of which he disapproves and which he has described in only the most superficial and inaccurate of ways.

It may safely be stated that, if the only reason for classifying Homœopathy as an occult therapy is a belief that there is no scientific explanation for the action of potencies above 12X, then this reason is no longer valid, and Homœopathy is freed from this stigma and can take its rightful place alongside accepted "scientific" healing modalities.

However, there is also the question of guilt by association, since Christian critics of Homœopathy are at pains to associate it with use of the pendulum, astrology, and other practices which might be described as "occult". As we have seen, such practices have nothing to do with Homœopathy itself. They are an aspect of the personal lives of those who choose to use them, and it is possible, indeed normal, to practise Homœopathy very effectively without them. Thus it is equally unjustifiable to label Homœopathy as "occult" on the grounds of this association. Great emphasis is placed on this association by writers of continental origin. However, people seeking treatment from registered homœopaths in the UK. should be assured that these practices have no part in the prescribed homœopathic studies here. Some individual homœopaths may choose to use them as adjuncts to their practice, but any patients who object to this should have no difficulty in finding another registered practitioner who practises "pure" Homœopathy.

REFERENCES:

1a/b. Taylor, M.: Private communication. 1993.

2. Bopp, H.J. *Homœopathy*. (Transl. Kilgore, M.) Great Joy Publications. Carryduff, Belfast. 2nd edition. 1985.

3. Peddie, J.C. *The Forgotten Talent*. Oldbourne 1961. Fontana 1966.

4. Dethlefsen T.: *Schicksal als Chance*. Goldmann. München. 1980.

5. Pfeifer, S. *Healing at any Price*. Word (UK) Ltd., Milton Keynes. 1988 (Engl. edition), (Original German edition, 1980)

6. Readers with a background in advanced science, especially Physics, who wish to read further on this topic may find the following of interest:

a) Schiff, M.: *The Memory of Water: Homœopathy and the Battle of Ideas in the New Science*. Thorsons. 1995.

b) Endler, P.C. & Schulte J.:*Ultra High Dilution - Physiology and Physics*. Kluwer Academic Publishers. Dordrecht / Boston / London. 1994 (very technical).

CHAPTER 7

NEED CHRISTIANS BE FEARFUL?

One of the things which impresses me deeply about the objections to natural therapies made by the Christian anti-occult lobby is the tremendous aura of fear which permeates them. Repeated references to demons and to occult contamination create an atmosphere of sinister peril, and remind me of some of the illustrations from an old edition of "Pilgrim's Progress" which I used to read as a child, in which Christian threaded his way along narrow paths, with writhing monsters reaching up to grab him and drag him down into the murky morass.

In Acts Chapter 15 Paul successfully argued before the leaders of the early Christian Church against burdening Gentile Christian converts with all the minutiæ of the Jewish law, "a yoke which neither we nor our fathers were able to bear". Likewise, in Acts Chapter 10, Peter had a vision in which he was told not to regard as unclean anything which God had made clean. Shortly afterwards he found himself in a situation in which, as a result of this message, he was able to free himself of his inbred prejudice against Gentile people and to agree to some of them being baptised. Thus we see that in the early formative days of the Christian Church, attitudes were being shaped and encouraged which observed the spirit rather than the letter of the Jewish law.

Indeed, such a shift in emphasis had been foreshadowed by Jesus himself in His teaching on Sabbath observance. Whilst keeping the Sabbath as a special day, He showed that it could still be used for performing compassionate tasks such as healing the sick and feeding the hungry (Luke 6:1-11) — actions which were clearly in accordance with the will of God. Jesus gave expression to the spirit of Christian piety in summing up the detail of the Ten Commandments in two "umbrella" commandments: Love the Lord your God.... and your neighbour as yourself. (Luke 10:27-28)

And yet so often we find a tendency in "biblical" objections to this or that to ignore the new spirit of Christ's teaching in favour of legalistic quotations from Old Testament legislative writing which was, after all, framed centuries before Christ for a people of an ancient civilisation whose circumstances were markedly different even from those of Christ's time, let alone the twentieth century A.D.

Even St. Paul, a man from a pharisaic background, can say to Timothy in I Timothy 4:1-7: "The spirit says expressly that in after times some will desert from the faith and give their minds to subversive doctrines inspired by devils, through the specious falsehoods of men whose own conscience is branded with the devil's sign. They forbid marriage and inculcate abstinence from certain foods, though God created them to be enjoyed with thanksgiving by believers who have inward knowledge of the truth. *For everything that God created is good*, [my emphasis], and nothing is to be rejected when it is taken with thanksgiving, since it is hallowed by God's own word and by prayer. By offering such advice as this to the brotherhood you will prove a good servant of Christ Jesus...... Have nothing to do with these godless myths, fit only for old women." In spite of the latter sentiment, hardly considered politically correct in modern times, Paul is affirming the inherent goodness of God's creation. The rejection of aspects of God's creation is condemned by Paul as "specious falsehood", and Christians are to be exhorted to enjoy the whole of God's creation with thanksgiving and reject none of it. And yet, in the writings which are directed against natural therapies by authors who would claim to be Christians, we are exhorted precisely to reject a whole portion of the spectrum of healing activity, because it is allegedly of the devil and therefore beyond God's control.

Are we to believe that God created electromagnetic energy solely for use by the devil? Why should any form of medicine which seeks to adjust the naturally occurring energy fields of living organisms automatically be stigmatised as demonic and separated from divine auspices? I must confess to some difficulty in grasping the logic of a so-called religious approach which sanctifies a system of medicine (Allopathy) which excludes any consideration of the spiritual dimension of man and advocates the cure of disease from a purely materialistic angle, whilst vilifying any system which operates from a holistic perspective and recognises that human kind is body, mind and spirit. The logic seems to be: Because we cannot see electromagnetic energy, and because its existence was first proposed and utilised in healing by Eastern cultures, it is therefore occult, and also demonic, and dangerous for Christians. (In earlier times, the superstitious attributed any phenomenon which arose from invisible causes to "magic" or "sorcery" or the devil. One does not expect such superstitious reactions from educated people in the twentieth century.)

Surely it is the Christian duty of such writers, having laid aside their orthodox medical prejudices and made a serious and open-minded study of the therapies they criticise, to exhort believers to accept these aspects of God's creation with thanksgiving, since they afford an opportunity of achieving health without the side effects of drugs and frequently unnecessary surgery. Instead, they abuse their influence to poison their readers' minds against a whole area of God's creation, and my contention is that, however sincere they may be, they do this from a position of orthodox medical prejudice, dressed up in arguments which some would consider sanctimonious.

An alternative possibility is that they are totally unaware of recent scientific study into electromagnetic energy fields, Quantum theory and the progress which has been made in the discipline of Biophysics, and are working from an outmoded model. In this case, of course, they are blind guides leading the blind, and leading them seriously astray, too; and the sooner they are exposed as such the better.

In Romans Chapter 14 we find references to vegetarianism among early Christians. The reason for their rejection of meat was nothing to do with the slaughter of or cruelty to animals. It was the fact that the meat available for sale had been offered to pagan gods and sacrificially or ritually slaughtered. The Jewish law contained strict regulations about the slaughter of animals, and it was closely tied up with sacrifice of any slaughtered animal to God, and with kosher preparation of meat, involving the removal of any blood before eating, since blood represented life. Thus in the Jewish tradition meat is a sensitive issue, and anyone whose roots were in that tradition would have a horror of eating meat which was not kosher, especially if it had been sacrificed to a pagan god. The mental association would be enough to spoil their meal and possibly put them in fear of divine punishment. In Romans 14, Paul counsels against the eating of meat or anything else which could be a stumbling block for someone else.

We have to follow our own consciences in such matters. However, he does refer to such "abstainers" as being "weaker" in their faith, and refers to some who have "faith enough to eat all kinds of foods". Again, in I Corinthians 10:v.25 ff., Paul says "You may eat anything sold in the meat market without raising questions of conscience; for the earth is the Lord's, and every-thing in it. If an unbeliever invites you to a meal and you care to go, eat whatever is put in front of you without raising questions of conscience. But if somebody says to you, 'This food has been offered in sacrifice', then out of consideration for him and for conscience' sake, do not eat it — not your conscience, I mean, but the other man's." Paul is talking about the power of mental association, and the importance of example and witness.

Such an argument could possibly be extended to systems of medical treatment. If a particular therapy became associated in a Christian's mind with something evil, then it would be wrong for that Christian to use it. If there was in fact nothing intrinsi-cally wrong with that system, then the sin would be that of the person who had created the mental association in the first place and deprived the Christian of its benefits. But Paul is clear that there is nothing intrinsically wrong with any aspect of God's creation; it is only mental associations which make something unacceptable.

No doubt some readers will wish to point out that Paul also cautions against passing moral judgements in this connection. "The man who eats must not hold in contempt the man who does not, and he who does not eat must not pass judgement on the one who does." I wish to make it quite clear that I am not holding in contempt those who refrain from using Homœopathy or other energy medicines because of fear of defilement or contamination. At the same time, I do feel strongly that, in the spirit of Paul's teaching, they should not pass judgement on others who do use such medicines. If someone had been able to come along and truthfully say to those Jews: "This meat is kosher and has not been offered to pagan gods", then no doubt many of them with a sigh of relief would have added meat to their diet. I am saying to those Christians who have been misled into thinking that Homœopathy is occult or satanic that this is demonstrably not so. If you are such a Christian, then I am telling you that you can be delivered from your fear and reservations and that it is possible to use this safe and gentle means of healing with joy, confidence and thanksgiving.

We see from Peter's vision in Acts Chapter 10 that even things which had formerly been regarded as unclean may become acceptable if the person can be released from the mental association. "Perfect love casteth out fear". Thus if we are filled with the love of Christ, we have no need to fear anything, as there will be no room in our hearts for evil influence. The Cross, a vile instrument of torture and death, was hallowed by God on Calvary and now, in the hearts of Christians, it is associated with their salvation, and is a symbol of the love of God.

There is a school of Christian thought which says that no act of healing can be from God unless it is performed specifically in the name of Jesus Christ. And if it is not from God, it must be of the devil. I have difficulty in accepting this rather dogmatic statement. In the whole area of healing worldwide, embracing all the treatments carried out by all the major medical systems in the world, including Allopathy, the number of healings carried out specifically in the name of Christ must be a tiny percentage indeed. It seems to me inconceivable and nonsensical that an essentially evil spiritual force should wish to remove so much suffering and do so much good. Why should it be considered impossible that God should inspire human beings — His own creation — to relieve each other's suffering? And what would Satan gain from inspiring them to do so? I cannot understand why some should wish to allow God only to be involved in healing within a tiny circumscribed area, and credit all other healing activity to Satan. I am reminded of Christ's words (Matthew 12) when he was accused by the Pharisees of casting out demons (i.e. healing) by the authority of Beelzebub. If this were so, He asserted, then it would mean that Satan's kingdom was divided and ripe for collapse.

It was unthinkable that healing, whether by His followers or by those of the Pharisees, could be the work of Satan, and it is unlikely that the Pharisees' followers were healing in the name of Christ. Why this fear that, unless a prescribed ritual is carried out, the process will be hi-jacked by Satan or by demons — a fear which is magnified a hundredfold if the healing activity is on any other level than the purely materialistic? Such a fearful attitude seems incompatible to me with confident, fearless Christianity. How can one go forward in faith and courage, filled with the Holy Spirit, if one is constantly looking over one's shoulder for demons?

In the epistle to the Romans (8:15-16), Paul speaks of the Spirit which Christians have received: "The Spirit you have received is not a spirit of slavery leading you back into a life of fear, but a Spirit that makes us sons, enabling us to cry 'Abba! Father!' In that cry the Spirit of God joins with our spirit in testifying that we are God's children; and if children, then heirs......" Thus, when one becomes a Christian, one leaves behind the life of fear and slavish adherence to sets of rules and laws, and steps out in confidence, responding with love and compassion in any situation into which one may be led and which provides an opportunity for Christian service. If one possesses a healing gift or tool (such as Homœopathy, Acupuncture, Reflexology,) as a Christian one will wish to offer it to the Lord and use it in His service. I can see no reason why God should not wish one of His children to use some knowledge which He has given regarding ways of restoring health, in order to relieve suffering.

Since the only evidence which seems to be forthcoming regarding the infiltration of healing activity by demons derives from personal revelation, I cannot help but find myself wondering about the source of this revelation and whether this is not actually one of Satan's ploys to divert the Church from doing what it should be doing. Satan must be cracking up with laughter at the sight of so many Christians refusing to benefit from healing modalities which would restore their health safely and effectively and turning instead to drugs with all their side-effects and suppression of symptoms compounding the problems and leading down the slippery slope towards chronic ill-health.

It has even been suggested that illness is a judgement, punishment or discipline from God, and we should leave well alone. This again I cannot accept, partly because Christ did not accept it. When Christ came across a life limited by disease or infirmity, His instinctive reaction seems to have been to remove it. When confronted by a woman with a spinal deformity, possibly osteoporosis, in Luke 13, He attributed this to Satan, not to God, and she was released from it.

Thus my suspicion is that, in their anxiety to impose their own allopathic prejudices against Natural Medicines upon other Christians, these writers have got things the wrong way round. It seems to me far more consistent with what the Bible teaches us about the nature of God through Jesus Christ that disease is of the devil and that healing, so long as it is performed in a spirit of compassionate concern for the patient, is of God. The transparent allopathic pride that emanates from so many passages in the books which purport to offer a Christian objection to Homœopathy and other therapies gives grounds for serious concern that the authors might be tainted by one of the seven deadly sins. In doing so they would of course lay themselves wide open to being used by Satan, no doubt unwittingly, to lead a whole section of the Church off on a wild goose-chase, turning many away not only from practising gentle healing modalities but also from benefiting, whilst sullying the reputation of those who seek to heal in a way which accords far more closely with the spirit of New Testament Christianity than does Allopathy. Satan must be highly satisfied at the general decline in the level of health in the western world which has coincided with the ascendancy of this "superior" branch of medicine. †

All this should not be taken as implying that all practitioners of Natural Therapies are without blemish in every respect. In an area in which there is still a comparative lack of regulation, openings exist for unscrupulous people with minimal qualifications to deceive and exploit. Patients seeking private treatment must therefore satisfy themselves as to the practitioner's training, credentials and insurance. Formal training in these therapies is a fairly recent institution, and there are still many experienced and gifted healers who learned their therapy by apprenticeship and have no certificates to hang on their walls. They will usually come well recommended by friends and neighbours. As far as Homœopathy is concerned, there are now colleges, and a professional body (The Society of Homœopaths) offering registration and professional insurance, and the same applies to the other major therapies such as Osteopathy, Chiropractic, Acupuncture and Herbal Medicine. (At the time of writing, the first two of these have had legislative recognition in the form of bills to establish legal regulation.)

Any member of any of these professions offering less than a professional service may be the subject of a formal complaint and disciplinary proceedings, and may be struck off their register. They will also have professional indemnity insurance in the case of any claim for negligence. Uninformed members of the allopathic establishment may claim that the whole of Natural Therapies is an unregulated jungle, but this is simply no longer the case. Even many of the less well-established therapies are now regulated through organisations such as the British Complementary Medicine Association. This means that intending patients may seek treatment with confidence, so long as they check their practitioner's credentials.

Let no-one think that I underestimate the power of Satan or the extent of modern-day practice of malevolent sorcery (also known as "black" magic). Nor would I decry the efforts of those

---

† "I'd just like to give you a few..........statistics which come from the N.H.S. of this country. The statistics say that malignant neoplasms — from 1961 to 1973, within 12 years — have increased almost 50%. 50% in 12 years! — in 100 years, what happens? The heart diseases have increased 54%; the nervous system diseases 36%; circulatory system, 24%; musculo-skeletal system, 36%." (George Vithoulkas — From Public Lecture, Sept.8th,1984, in London.) And that did not include AIDS!

who seek to protect the innocent from entanglement in them. My argument is, I hope, clear by now, and it is this: that by seeking to find or create an association between sorcery and energy medicine, Christian writers are on a wild goose chase and, in view of recent discoveries in the field of Biophysics, they should withdraw and look elsewhere for more convincing evidence of Satan's work and demonic influence. They would also be well advised to follow the trend within the medical profession of recognising that other therapies than Allopathy may have something of value to offer the patient, and desist from their position of tunnel vision and allopathic supremacy, showing a little more Christian humility and even charity towards their partners in genuine healing.

Paul, writing to the Corinthians (I Cor.1:27), says: ".....God hath chosen the foolish things of the world to confound the wise; and God hath chosen the weak things of the world to confound the things which are mighty, and base things of the world, and things which are despised, hath God chosen, yea, and *things which are not, to bring to nought things that are.*" (My emphasis). He could almost have been writing about Homœopathy!

POTENTIZATION

This appendix looks at the preparation of homœopathic remedies and the related issues in some technical detail.

In order to understand how homœopathic remedies work on the dynamic level, it is necessary to appreciate how they are produced.

Let us suppose that a homœopathic pharmacist wishes to prepare Belladonna from source. He will procure a sample of Deadly Nightshade which is of good quality and free from pollutants, and will macerate it in ethanol for a while before removing the spent plant material to leave a mother tincture. This tincture is extremely poisonous and would not be prescribed. When he first began practising homœopathy, Hahnemann originally used gross doses of his selected medicines, often with distressing results. He therefore set about reducing the size of his doses systematically, so as to minimise his patients' suffering. He diluted the medicines serially, and found that whilst the side-effects were eliminated, the effectiveness of the medicines was not.

As already mentioned in Chapter 2: "How Homœopathy Developed", the story goes that, on one occasion, a vial of medicine fell out of Hahnemann's bag and remained unnoticed for some time on the floor of his carriage where, owing to the state of the roads in Germany at the time, it received a good shaking-up. When he eventually retrieved it and started using it, he found its effectiveness much enhanced, and resolved in future to incorporate a good shaking into the preparation of his remedies.

Thus the pharmacist will take one part of the mother tincture, dilute it with 99 parts of ethanol, and "succuss" it (i.e. shake it up) with a series of sharp movements of the vial, to produce the "first potency". (Some pharmacies employ a machine to do this succussion, others prefer to do it manually.)

[I should mention also that there are other scales of potentization than the one described here. I am describing the centesimal scale, in which each stage involves a dilution of 1:100. There is also the decimal scale, involving dilutions of 1:10, in which case the stages are denoted by the suffix "X" in the UK. and by the prefix "D" on the continent (e.g 6X, D6). Further scales, such as the LM or "Q" are also in use, but the basic pharmaceutical process is the same.]

One part of the first potency is then taken, diluted with a further 99 parts of ethanol, and succussed again to produce the second potency. Then the process is repeated to produce the third potency, and so on ad infinitum. Very toxic substances such as Belladonna, Aconite or snake poisons may not be dispensed in potencies lower than about 6.

Minerals, and other substances which may not easily be soluble in ethanol, go through a different process in the lower potencies. These will be "triturated" (i.e. ground up with lactose using a pestle and mortar), still in the proportions described above (e.g. one part of gold leaf to 99 parts of lactose to produce the remedy *Aurum*) until a stage is reached where the original substance is so diluted and subsumed in the lactose that it becomes soluble in ethanol. (This stage is reached at around the third or fourth potency). The importance of the ethanol lies in its use to medicate the pills and powders which are the normal vehicles of homœopathic prescribing. A few drops of the alcoholic medicating potency are added to the vial of unmedicated lactose pills, which are suffused with the vapour and become medicines. Some homœopaths find liquid potencies more effective, and these are also more suitable for lactose-intolerant patients. In this case the ethanol potency will be diluted with water to make it more palatable.

Whether succussion or trituration is used, it should be clear to anyone with an elementary knowledge of physics that there is a transfer of physical energy taking place here. What is less clear is exactly how the transfer of energy modifies the frequency of the original substance. That such a modification takes place is strongly suggested by the fact that any potency of any remedy can be "synthesised" electro-magnetically using a machine, originally devised by Malcolm Rae, in which unmedicated lactose tablets or ethanol are subjected to an electromagnetic field whose frequency can be predetermined by the setting of dials. Tablets produced by this method will facilitate the same healing processes in the patient as will remedies prepared by the traditional method, although there is a lack of agreement among homœopaths as to how long they remain effective, and whether they are the same thing as a traditionally produced remedy.

It is perhaps also of interest that some practitioners administer remedies by olfaction (i.e. sniffing from the bottle), or even transcutaneously (by rubbing on the skin), again to no less effect. Thus it appears that the healing "message" of the remedy can trigger a healing response in the patient via the olfactory nerve, in the same way as does the vapour of an Aromatherapy oil or, like the latter, with a direct physiological action as a result of absorption via the skin.

It has to be pointed out that having reached the twelfth centesimal (or twenty-fourth decimal) potency, it is highly unlikely that a potentized remedy will still contain any molecules of the original substance. It nevertheless remains effective. Scientifically conducted studies have established that such preparations relieve symptoms more effectively than a placebo(1), although such studies generally evaluate the effectiveness of potentized remedies rather than the homœopathic method of prescribing. The accepted conditions for scientific trials of medicines require that all the participating people take the same drug (apart from the control group who take placebo). Homœopathic treatment is strongly individualised, and it is highly unlikely in real practice that a number of people with the same health problem would all be prescribed the same remedy. This underscores how unreasonable are the repeated demands from the scientific establishment that homœopathic medicines should undergo the same proofs of effectiveness as conventional drugs. Alternative protocols are required which reflect the different basis of prescription so that, for example, each member of the group receiving a remedy in the trial would receive the remedy which was actually homœopathically indicated for him or her, while the control group would still receive placebo.

It is potentization which carries Homœopathy beyond the bounds of credibility for many people with a background or training in orthodox, materialistic science. How can a preparation which contains no molecules of the original substance remain effective against disease? Surely its action must rely on the placebo effect. Such a point of view raises two issues.

Firstly, it is based on biochemical rather than biophysical thinking. As we have already seen, it is energy which controls the chemical processes of the human organism, not biochemistry. Molecules are not necessarily required. In a study published in 1988 which has become famous (or infamous, depending on which school of thought you support), the French scientist Jacques Benveniste(2) established that the biochemical anti-IgE, diluted well beyond the molecular level (up to $1:10^{120}$) brings about the same basophil degranulation response in blood samples as does undiluted anti-IgE. The same results were replicated in other laboratories in Israel, Canada and Italy.

Almost more impressive than this result were the frenzied efforts of the scientific establishment (as embodied by "Nature", the periodical in which the study was published) to discredit it. The Editor went on television to give an interview which made it clear that a major risk of accepting this result would be the possible validation of Homœopathy, a therapy against which he clearly held a strong and transparent personal prejudice. Accompanied by a scientific fraud-buster and a magician, he betook himself off to Benveniste's laboratory in Paris, to return with "evidence" that the results had been mistaken, although it is not clear how all the other laboratories could also have produced the same mistaken results(3). Subsequent work by Benveniste showed that when the "potentised" anti-IgE, had its electromagnetic field destroyed by placing it inside an electric coil, it no longer had any effect on the basophil degranulation response (part of allergic response).

Secondly, in nature, quantity is not necessarily equal to quality. In fact sometimes they may appear to be in inverse proportion. Whether or not we approve of animal experiments, Lashley found that rats could still remember how to run a maze when over 90% of their brain cortex had been removed. John Lorber found that a patient, a gifted mathematician with an IQ of 130, was suffering from hydrocephalus, with about 98% of the brain tissue required for thinking replaced by fluid (4). This fluid, like Benveniste's diluted anti-IgE, had somehow retained a memory of the thought-patterns already learnt. Thus it should not be thought too surprising, nor indeed impossible, for a homœopathic potency, diluted beyond the molecular level, to retain a memory of the energy-frequency of the substance which was once dissolved in it(5).

It should by now be clear that, in considering the potentization of homœopathic medicines, we are dealing with matters scientific, albeit not yet fully understood. It is easy to see how such matters could be superstitiously ascribed to the supernatural by those whose understanding of science is on a purely materialistic, Cartesian level. Various scientific and technological inventions, e.g. printing and radio, have been attributed to the devil, although nowadays we use them every day and give thanks for them. Science, if it is to maintain its integrity, must take account of such phenomena as electromagnetic fields; indeed the work of Popp, Smith, Piccardi and others is already doing so, and those who persist in attributing biophysical phenomena to the supernatural are increasingly being overtaken and left behind.

REFERENCES:

1. e.g.The Lancet 18.10.86 — *Is Homœopathy a placebo response?* by David T.Reilly et al.),

2. Benveniste J. et al.: (Research Report) in *Nature No. 333*, Pp. 816-818. 30.6.88

3. MacEoin D.: The Denaturing of Science. *Journal of Alternative & Complementary Medicine* Vol.6 No.9 Sept.1988. (This article, discussing Nature's response to Benveniste's findings and the related issues, gives a very useful bibliography of research references.)

4. Quoted in Chopra D.: *Quantum Healing.* Bantam, New York. 1989. (Pp. 147-8).

5. Schiff M.: *The Memory of Water: Homœopathy and the Battle of Ideas in the New Science.* Thorsons. 1995.

RESEARCH BY FRITZ-ALBERT POPP

This Appendix describes in some technical detail the German research by Fritz-Albert Popp† referred to in Chapter 3: "Energy Medicine and the Vital Force"

Working at the University of Kaiserslautern on a project commissioned by the former West German government to establish the effectiveness of homœopathic treatment, the biophysicist Fritz-Albert Popp demonstrated that potentized remedies such as are used in Homœopathy could affect the emission of photons from plant seedlings. Photons are manifestations of electro-magnetic fields and their emission (also known as "Low-level Luminescence") shows a close correlation with many fundamental life-processes of living biological systems (e.g. cell reproduction, immunological reactions, stress reactions). Popp devised an apparatus which can detect and measure the photon emission of plant seedlings, showing it as a continuous print-out.

His experiments showed quite clearly that the rate of photon emission was changed by the application to the seedlings of a potentized remedy in a saline solution base, whereas that of control samples given the saline solution only (i.e. a placebo) remained unchanged. His experiments were based on the principle that it is the distribution and organisation of energy across the structure of a biological system which regulates the biochemical processes of that system (plant, animal etc.), and showed that the action of potentized remedies on any biological system is via its energy fields. Biophysics is therefore of greater importance than Biochemistry in the study of living organisms, and certainly in the study of their healing.

This agrees with the studies of Burr and Ravitz, referred to in Chapter 3. Hahnemann states that disease is the result of an untuning of the Vital Force, and therefore something which occurs on the dynamic (energy) level. This being the case, in order to be effective, treatment must also be given on the dynamic level. Popp's work (and also Cyril Smith's work with allergic patients, referred to in Chapter 3), shows that it is possible to do this, and that potentized remedies, transmitting energy on a very subtle level, will affect the energy field frequencies of living beings.

Another interesting aspect of Popp's research concerned cultured tumour cells (wish cells). When cytostatic (anti-cancer) drugs were applied to the cells, their growth-rate increased. When biological remedies were applied, the results varied: in gross doses they increased the growth-rate; when given in micro-doses (as used in Homœopathy), the growth of the cells was inhibited. When Iscador was applied — an anthroposophical cytostatic made from mistletoe and normally injected in microdoses — the cell growth-rate could only be inhibited.

Popp regarded this as the best experimental demonstration to date of the Arndt-Schulz Law, which states that small stimuli encourage life-activity, medium-strong stimuli tend to impede it, and very strong stimuli are apt to stop or destroy it. (The growth of tumour cells of course represents a threat to life activity, so anything which inhibits their growth will favour life activity in the organism which is host to the tumour.) The Arndt-Schulz Law supports the use in Homœopathy of microdoses (small stimuli). It was however propounded by two orthodox scientists with no homœopathic axe to grind: Professor Arndt was an eminent biologist and Professor Schulz was a leading pharmacologist.

---

†. Popp F.A.: Bericht an Bonn. Verlag für Ganzheitsmedizin, Essen. 1986. [For an appreciation, see Crook A.R.: Article in "The Homœopath" Vol.8 No.4 (1989)].

DEFINITIONS AND EXPLANATIONS OF TERMS USED

Where a definition has already been given, reference is made to its page number.

Acupuncture   A part of Traditional Chinese Medicine which balances the energy flow within the body by using very fine needles to stimulate points situated on the energy meridians. The nature of the energy imbalance is diagnosed by taking a number of pulses, observation of the tongue and facial features and various other methods.

Adrenalin(e)   A hormone secreted by the adrenal glands (near the kidneys). Its effects include increasing the rate at which the heart beats, raising the blood-pressure and blood sugar level, and increasing the blood supply to the muscles; i.e. assisting a physical response to stressful situations.

Allopathy   The system of medicine based on curing by opposites. Also known as Western or Orthodox Medicine.

Alternative medicine   (See Page 5.) The distinction between this and Complementary Medicine (q.v.) is often ignored or deliberately blurred by those who wish to avoid giving offence to the orthodox medical establishment.

Anthroposophical Medicine   Medicine practised according to the teachings of Rudolf Steiner. Some use is made of potentized remedies, but the philosophy differs from that of Homœopathy.

Aromatherapy   The medicinal use of essential oils distilled from various parts of plants and trees. In the UK. the usual medium is massage, and internal use of the oils is discouraged because of their strength. The oils may also be used in vaporisers, baths, inhalations and compresses, and their effect is on the brain via the olfactory nerve (q.v.) as well as via the skin.

Ayurvedic Medicine   The traditional system of medicine in India. Treatment is according to constitutional types called Doshas, and includes dietary regulation as well as prescription of natural medicines.

Basophil Degranulation Response   A biochemical response, part of an allergic reaction.

Biofeedback   The use of instruments, usually attached to the body, to provide the patients with ongoing information regarding their physical responses during activities or treatment.

Chronology   (as on Page 21)   The sequence of time.

Classical Homœopathy   The use of one homœopathically selected remedy at a time (as distinct from Complex Homœopathy -q.v.) Some Homœopaths may use a particularly narrow interpretation of this term to denote only one of the various classical methodologies (usually that of J. T. Kent, a famous American homœopath).

Complementary Medicine   (See Page 5). Therapies with which Orthodox medical treatment does not interfere when used concurrently. Homœopathy does not normally fall within this category.

Complex Homœopathy   The use of medication consisting of several potentized remedies combined into one dose. This is common on the Continent, but is really a separate therapy from Classical Homœopathy as described in this book.

Double-blind trial　See Page 16.

Dualism　The separation of medical and spiritual matters. (See Page 21)

Empirical　Based on experiment, not on theory.

Endoscopy　Examination of the interior of the bowels by insertion of a tube incorporating illumination and a viewing device.

Ethanol　A type of alcohol, used in the preparation of mother tinctures and liquid potencies in homœopathic pharmacy.

Flagellation　Whipping or scourging oneself as a form of religious discipline.

Hydrocephalus　"Water on the brain". The presence of fluid within the cranial cavity

IgE　Immunoglobulin

Kinetic Energy　Energy resulting from movement. When a bus or train slows down suddenly it is kinetic energy which throws the standing passengers forward.

Lactose　Sugar of milk.Used as the basis for most homœopathic tablets.

Lateral Thinking　A way of thinking devised by Edward de Bono, which liberates the thinker from the rigidity of one single and maybe obvious approach to a problem or question.

Mastitis　Inflammation of the breasts or udders.

Materia Medica　Book containing the symptom pictures of remedies as derived from provings (q.v.).

Molecule　A combination of atoms forming a definite substance. E.g. one zinc atom combined with one oxygen atom is one molecule of zinc oxide.

New Age To do with the Age of Aquarius. The belief is that the Age of Pisces, which is currently drawing to a close, has been characterised by the growth of materialism and institutional activities. The Age of Aquarius which is now beginning, will be characterised by spiritual values, non-violence and group activities.

Occult See Page 45.

Olfactory Nerve The nerve situated in the nasal cavity which is responsible for the sense of smell.

Oncologist A doctor or surgeon specialising in the treatment of cancer.

Placebo Effect A phenomenon, known in most systems of medicine, by which an unmedicated pill or other dummy treatment will result in a curative or beneficial effect. It is assumed that this is because of an unconscious mental process in the patient.

Post-partum Hæmorrhage Bleeding, usually serious, from the womb following childbirth.

Proving The taking of a substance by healthy human volunteers to establish which symptoms it produces and will therefore cure when used medicinally.

Reductionism The splitting up of a subject or topic into subdivisions for greater convenience of study, thus losing sight of the totality.

Reflexology The treatment of patients by massaging zones on the feet (or hands) which are linked in some non-material way with other organs or systems of the body. The results can be dramatic.

Repertory A book or computer system used by homœopaths as an index of the symptoms which are caused/cured by homœopathic medicines.

Research Protocol The procedure to be followed during a research investigation or trial.

Resonance   An example would be: Two people stand in a room each holding a tuning fork tuned to the same note. When one tuning fork is struck, the one held by the other person will also sound without being struck. Two tuning forks tuned to different notes would not do this, because they do not resonate together. For resonance to occur, the two or more instruments involved must be attuned.

Sacred Prostitution   Historically, the practice whereby followers of a particular religion would have sexual intercourse with priests or priestesses of that religion, usually at a temple or holy place, in the belief that this would be of spiritual benefit.

Saline Solution   Salt solution.

Sanctimonious   Making a show of piety; sounding pompously pious.

Septicæmia   The presence in the blood of multiplying microbes.

Suppression   The reversal, normally by medication, of the body's natural tendency to detoxify itself from within outwards. One example is the suppression of eczema by skin creams, resulting in asthma. Another is the prevention of acute disease (e.g. by mass vaccination programmes) resulting in widespread chronic diseases. (See footnote to Page 63). Whilst the concept of suppression is of great importance in Homœopathy, it is not recognised in Orthodox medicine. (This is a strong reason for designating Homœopathy as an alternative, rather than a complementary therapy.)

T-lymphocyte   A type of white blood-cell, important for immune defence.

SUMMARY

MAIN OBJECTIONS WITH SUGGESTED REPLIES:

Most of the books objecting to homœopathy on Christian grounds are written or co-written by doctors of orthodox medicine from the point of view that it is superior to other forms of medicine. From the way they are written it is clear that the authors are far from impartial and have a scientific axe to grind.

No. 1. Potentization suffuses the remedies with occult power and makes them dangerous.
It has been shown scientifically that liquids can carry a "memory" of the electromagnetic energy pattern of a substance which was previously dissolved in them, and of which no molecules remain. Water can also be charged with the electromagnetic frequency of an allergen and used to relieve allergy symptoms when carried by the patient. Thus there is a scientific explanation for the action of ultra-molecular potencies. To attribute the action to occult power is superstitious, and there is no reason, either scientific or religious, for doing this.

No. 2. Because some homœopaths use divination, homœopathy is an occult practice.
Using a pendulum or any other means of divination is a part of an individual's private philosophy of life. It is no part of homœopathic practice as taught in Colleges and described in textbooks. The majority of homœopaths practise without a pendulum, and its use could be regarded as a sign of inadequate skill/training. Because some people go to work by bicycle, this does not mean that the bicycle is the only means of getting to work.

No. 3. Vital Force is an oriental, non-Christian concept, and Christians who have anything to do with it will get mixed up in oriental religions and be susceptible to demonic influence.
Biophysics has shown that every living being possesses an electromagnetic energy field. This controls all the organism's vital functions, and if its resonance is disturbed, the vital functions are disturbed. This energy was first observed by Chinese and Indian physicians. They did not invent it; it is a natural phenomenon. It is neither the invention nor the property of any one culture, religion or philosophy. Because Western orthodox medicine deals only with physical, materialistic aspects of the human organism, it has chosen to overlook it, but every other major system of medicine in the world takes it into account. There is nothing occult or demonic about it, and there is no reason to fear it.

No. 4. Homœopathy is disreputable because of certain aspects of Hahnemann's life.
The aspect usually objected to is Freemasonary. In Hahnemann's time it was routine for all brilliant and original thinkers to become Masons. There was no perceived conflict with their Christian beliefs. Hahnemann was a Christian. Much of the chaos and misfortune which occurred in his life was contributed to by the persecution which he suffered at the hands of the medical and pharmaceutical professions.

No. 5. Hahnemann's proving of quinine could not be repeated, and the whole of Homœopathy is therefore an inventor's error.
What is important about Homœopathy is the Principle of Similars, not one particular proving. The Principle of Similars has been successfully applied in healing by homœopaths in countless thousands of cases, and was being used before Hahnemann as well. As for provings, results vary between provers, depending on their individual susceptibilities, and the total results are pooled. Provings are different from a scientific experiment, which must be repeatable and which depersonalizes those taking part.

No. 6. Homœopathy is non-Christian because of its association with the New Age movement, which is inspired by Eastern mysticism and Astrology.
Homœopathy was in use well before the New Age movement and did not grow from it. The fact that many New Age sympathizers use Homœopathy does not make it a New Age therapy, any more than the use of allopathy by English people in Europe makes it a solely English system of medicine.

No. 7. Some homœopaths use astrology. This means that is is non-Christian and Christians should avoid contamination by it.
As with divination, the use of astrology by anyone is a question of their philosophy of life, and has nothing to do with Homœopathy in itself. It does not make sense to condemn a whole profession simply because a minority of its members does something of which we may disapprove. Any Christian patient who wishes not to have contact with astrology should check with the homœopath before starting treatment, and go to another practitioner if necessary.

No. 8. Homœopathy claims to be a spiritual medicine. Spiritual matters should be left to the Church. Non-experts dabbling in spiritual matters may defile the Christian patient's spirit.
The fact that Homœopathy recognises that human beings are body, mind and spirit does not make it a spiritual practice or a religion. It is not in competition with the Church. Allopathy is alone among the world's major medical systems in dealing only with the physical aspect of the human being. Many consider this to be a shortcoming.

It should be noted that when Hahnemann uses the word "spiritual" in his writings, it is in the sense of 'non-material and dynamic', and does not have a religious sense. It is possible that the mistaken idea of homœopathy claiming to be a 'spiritual practice' comes from this being taken out of context.

CONCLUSION

St. Paul, in I Timothy 4:1-7, says that everything in God's creation is good and should be enjoyed with thanksgiving. He criticises those who say that believers should abstain from this and not use that, and calls rejection of any aspect of God's creation "specious falsehood". In Romans he also refers to those who abstained from meat which had unclean associations as "weak in the faith", and says that those who are "strong in the faith" will eat anything. Christians who feel that there is something "unclean" or "occult" about Homœopathy may now be reassured that there is nothing supernatural about it. It makes use of laws of science provided by God as part of His creation for the healing of suffering people and animals, and is an aspect of His providence. In fact, I believe it to be perfectly possible that the idea of Homœopathy being occult or satanic was sown in people's minds by Satan himself as a way of frustrating the fulfilment of God's will.

USEFUL
ADDRESSES

PACT (Positive Approach to Complementary Therapies)
c/o Breath Ministries,
Revd. J. Huggett,
"Chilston Mead",
Pembury Road,
Tunbridge Wells, Kent TN2 3QN
*PACT issues a Register of Christian practitioners of
alternative and complementary therapies.*

The Society of Homœopaths,
2 Artizan Road,
Northampton NN1 4HU
Tel: 01604 21400
Send an A5 sae for a list of qualified homœopaths in your area.